Mott MacDonald has been a leading consultant in the planning, design and implementation of rapid transit systems for over 20 years. Our expertise, ranging from modern light rail schemes to heavy mass transit, has taken us to many of the world's larger cities.

We played a key role in the UK's first 'light' rail system in Tyne and Wear and have been consultants to Greater Manchester PTE since 1980. Our current workload includes a major involvement in the development of the Docklands Light Railway and other light rail schemes and proposals for major cities throughout the UK and overseas.

Backed by a wealth of experience, we can offer clients an unrivalled service in all aspects of modern light rail transit projects:

- Conceptual and feasibility studies including demand modelling and revenue forecasting

- Preparation of Parliamentary submissions and funding applications

- Planning and design of route, tunnelling and ventilation

- Power supplies and OHLE

- Signalling and telecommunications

- Remote control and ticketing systems

- Rolling stock design, layout, specification and operation

- Safety engineering and management

- Project management, line management and control of operations

- System integration, operation, staffing and recruitment

- Market research and environmental assessment

If you would like to know more about our services, please contact our Associates:

Tim Morton (Transportation Planning) or
John Corrie (Railway Systems)

Mott MacDonald Group
St Anne House
20-26 Wellesley Road
Croydon CR9 2UL

Telephone : 081 686 5041
Fax: 081 681 5706/081 688 1814

Mott MacDonald

MOVE FORWARD WITH

BRIWAY

High Performance   Versatile

Cost Effective   Environmentally Friendly

Modular Construction   Local Assembly

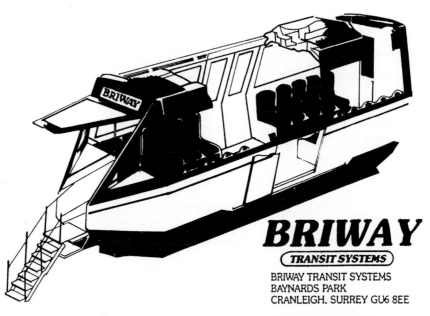

BRIWAY
TRANSIT SYSTEMS

BRIWAY TRANSIT SYSTEMS
BAYNARDS PARK
CRANLEIGH, SURREY GU6 8EE

Telephone: (0483) 277170
Telex 859068 AEBRIS G
Fax: (0483) 275037

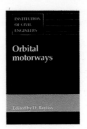

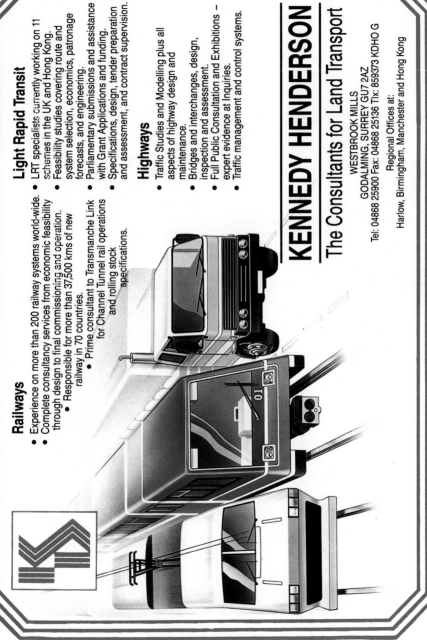

VonRoll MONORAIL

the transport system of the future

- whisper quiet
- pollution free
- space efficient

- high passenger attraction
- versatile
- proven system

a new and exciting perspective on city travel

Light transit systems

Proceedings of the symposium on the potential of light transit systems in British cities organized by the Institution of Civil Engineers and held in Nottingham on 14–15 March 1990

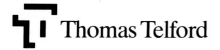
Thomas Telford

Co-sponsored by the Institution of Mechanical Engineers, the Institution of Electrical Engineers and the Light Rail Transit Association

Organizing Committee: B. H. North (chairman), P. D. Longhurst, J. H. Palmer and A. P. Young

British Library Cataloguing in Publication Data
Light transit systems
  1. Urban regions. Light railway passenger transport services
  388.42
1SBN 0-7277-1590-9

Published for the Institution of Civil Engineers by Thomas Telford Ltd, Telford House, 1 Heron Quay, London E14 9XF.

Printed and bound in Great Britain by Mackays of Chatham

Contents

Opening address

D. A. GRAHAM, CBE, Director General, Greater Manchester
Passenger Transport Executive

I was somewhat daunted to be giving the keynote address at
this symposium because I feared that many of those present –
and certainly many of the authors – knew a lot more about
light rail than I do. However, having been involved with the
Manchester Metrolink scheme for many years, and having been a
Vice-president of UITP, I have some experience of light rail,
both here and abroad.

From the number of delegates at the symposium it is clear
that interest in light rail schemes in Britain is at an
extremely high level. My own executive is probably spending
about £500 000 on development alone and, therefore, the
industry which has grown up to plan, design and evaluate these
schemes must already have a turnover which is measurable in
millions. What I would like to do is to make it clear why
there is such interest. By trying to understand the light
rail phenomenon in a broader context I hope that this address
will lay the foundation for the rest of the volume.

One fact about light railways, which range from street
tramways to segregated railways, is that they are not new.
Even in this country Tyne & Wear Metro has many of the
characteristics of a light railway, although it is fully
segregated and runs in tunnel for part of its length. But if
we look abroad, as we should, we find an extensive array of
light rail systems. For example, Mr Joos' paper tells us
something about the extensive network in his own city of
Zurich, which is a good example of a long established light
railway. So we cannot really explain the interest in light
rail by claiming that it is new technology filling the gap in
our existing system.

I believe that the reasons for the interest in light rail go
much deeper than this and can be traced back to a number of
factors governing transport policy. The first is the pressure
to improve efficiency and reduce costs. The Greater
Manchester Transport Executive's evaluation of the Manchester
Metrolink showed very clearly that with light rail it is

Light transit systems. Thomas Telford, London, 1990

possible to operate much higher frequencies at much the same operating cost levels as a conventional British Rail service. In effect, we are getting 30% more train miles for the same cost as the existing BR services. Light rail can, therefore, make a major contribution to increasing efficiency.

A second, related factor is that it is becoming increasingly clear that conventional railway is developing increasingly sophisticated rolling stock and services that are aimed at servicing longer distance travel demands. The provincial express network is a good example. In these circumstances it is becoming less easy to dovetail local services into this network - especially when demand for long distance services, inter city and provincial, is growing - unless significant capital expenditures are incurred. Thus, to continue to offer an attractive, high frequency, regular service on many BR lines is becoming increasingly expensive. This increases the incentive to look for alternative solutions. Although many people may believe that in Manchester we just happen to choose the Altrincham and Bury lines, I can assure you that the fact that it will take local services off the sector of track between Piccadilly and Deansgate stations in the city centre is part of the overall rail strategy for Manchester. This releases track capacity which can then be used by longer distance services.

A third reason - at least in the areas where it is possible to convert BR lines to light rail - is that much of the rolling stock faces renewal. Again, this was a significant factor in the Manchester case: we would have had to spend about £20 million just to renew the existing fleets of electric trains on the Bury and Altrincham lines. Thus, a thorough review of options had to be undertaken, from which light rail emerged as clearly the best available to us. We chose light rail for sound, economic reasons.

My fourth reason for the level of interest in light rail is that passengers want higher quality public transport, just as they want higher quality in the other goods and services they consume. The success of many minibus services has illustrated this at one level. Light rail offers a higher quality in respect of the vehicles, journey times, frequency and access to destinations than either bus or conventional rail. Bearing in mind the limited scope for increasing the quality of conventional public transport, the importance of light rail in this context must not be underestimated. It is a means of giving the passengers what they are increasingly demanding. This leads me to the fifth reason: light rail is perceived as an attractive alternative to the private car for some journeys. It is significant that in many cities abroad there is much greater use of public transport than there is in this country, despite higher car ownership levels. I would like to

quote from the Economist Europe city guide entry for Zurich
'most people (top executives included) walk or take trams in
the centre of Zurich'! Proof, if ever there was any, that
light rail can be an attractive alternative to the car.

It is this which, I believe, may now be the main reason for
the level of interest in light rail investment that we are now
experiencing. Urban traffic continues to grow. Since
deregulation in 1986, bus patronage in the metropolitan
countries has declined by 16%. The bus may not prove to be an
adequate alternative to the car for five reasons:

(1)   It is even more badly affected by congestion than the
        car. For example, the disruptions on a trip affected by
        congestion can affect passengers on several subsequent
        trips. Thus operating costs, and as a result fares,
        increase as a result of congestion.

(2)   Its productivity is limited by the average speed of
        traffic which, as congestion increases, will fall.
(3)   Even in congested conditions productivity of both
        drivers and vehicles are constrained by vehicle size.
        In the future, the real operating costs per bus
        passenger will continue to increase. As a result, fares
        will rise in real terms.

(4)   The bus does not offer an in-vehicle environment which
        car users perceive as attractive.

(5)   Buses are increasingly less able to gain access to city
        centres - the destination of most people.

As urban traffic grows, congestion will get worse and last
for more of the day. Already there is clear evidence that the
length of the peak on the roads is increasing in many cities.
As the Government appears to recognize, road building can
never keep pace with the growth in road traffic. Therefore,
increasing the capacity of public transport as an attractive
alternative to the car will become an ever more important part
of the urban transport scheme.

My conclusion is that the upsurge of interest in light rail
is for the reasons I have outlined to you. It is not as some
academic commentators have alleged, because PTEs and the
politicians on the PTAs wish to have direct operational
control of another mode of transport to make up for losing the
buses. To begin with, people have broader horizons than just
running buses or light rail. In addition, it is unlikely that
with the present Government there would be any direct PTE or
local authority operation, although the PTEs still have the
powers to do so.

Finally, I would also like to draw attention to what I believe needs to be done for the role of light rail to be optimized in the future. I believe that the most important thing is to recognize the potential of improved public transport, including light rail, as an alternative to the car, at a time of rapidly rising traffic congestion in urban areas. Secondly, we need some continuity of funding, even where it is a case of the treasury just allowing local government to spend its own money through the credit approvals system. The hand-to-mouth way in which the Treasury controls public expenditure is totally inappropriate for developing any investment in urban transport. We have a roads programme and need to develop a public transport investment programme for each major urban area. Only when we do this will we start to be able sensibly to trade off investment in roads and public transport.

Thirdly, we need a consistent way of evaluating roads and public transport investments. While I am given to understand that the Section 56 grant criteria can in some way be made consistent with the cost-benefit analysis used for roads, I find it hard to follow the logic and to believe it. A consistent framework based on cost-benefit analysis is required, and the papers in chapter 2 deal with this in more depth.

Fourthly, we must recognize that both the public and the private sectors have roles in the future development of urban public transport. Few people can be so naive as to believe that light rail schemes can be funded totally commercially from start to finish - even the Avon scheme is looking for a Section 56 grant. Equally, it may be foolish totally to ignore the private sector. However, flexibility is needed in defining the roles of the two sectors and bringing them together in such a way that both get an adequate reward for their investments, even though it may be in the form of private sector profit and community benefits for the public sector. Much more needs to be learned about this and each case has to be taken on its merits.

Looking at the impressive list of papers which comprise this volume, I feel sure that it will advance our understanding of the light rail alternative.

1. Light transit proposals in British cities: a review

M. R. TAPLIN, MCIT, Chairman, Light Rail Transit Association

SYNOPSIS.   Following the success of the Tyne & Wear Metro
and   Docklands Light Railway, and the experience of new
systems in North America, light transit has been suggested
as the solution to both transport and inner city problems
in British urban areas. This review identifies the current
and credible schemes and summarises their characteristics.
The October 1989 submission date for this paper will result
in updating for presentation in March 1990; in particular
it is written without final information on Parliamentary
approvals at the end of the 1988/89 session, or details of
Bill submissions in November 1989 for the 1989/90 session.

WHAT IS LIGHT TRANSIT ?
1   Some confusion is possible on the meaning of light
transit, particularly since the initials LRT are often
used, standing for light rapid transit or light rail
transit. Light rapid transit was a North American term used
as a differential from heavy rapid transit, which itself
has now been largely superceded by the term metro. Once
other than rail-based systems came on the scene, light rail
transit was used to distinguish the technology of steel
wheel / steel rail systems, and light rapid transit covered
the whole field of guided passenger transit systems with
characteristics not conforming to those of what the British
Department of Transport calls main line railways.

2   Semantics   apart,   lightness   implies   several
characteristics. Less demanding construction parameters and
hence reduced cost and build time, lighter vehicles and
structures, sharper curves, steeper gradients, more
flexibility to fit into the urban environment, and lower
operating costs. These may not in total always be true of
every system, for in practice there is no clear dividing
line between light transit and metro, as many continental
cities demonstrate; it is also possible to "gold plate" a
light transit system.

3   The systems under development or study in Great Britain are predominately light rail transit. This is because it is a proven system with measured success around the world, it is not patented, and it is the only guided system with the flexibility to run on any alignment from the street to the main line railway. If the mixed operation implied by the latter is at present a stumbling block with the DTp Railway Inspectorate, then Nottingham's twin city of Karlsruhe is about to show how it can be done.

4   10 years after the opening of the Tyne & Wear system, there are three publically-operated light transit systems in operation, one under construction and three more authorised. Others are being designed and many more investigated. All are described below and shown on the map.

BLACKPOOL
5   The sole survivor of British urban tramways runs over 18 km of largely segregated track carrying about 6 million passengers/annum and providing a regular service throughout the year as well as being a summer tourist attraction. The Blackpool seafront alignment is almost wholly unfenced roadside reservation (with one short section of street track); the line is then on fenced private right-of-way to the nearby market town of Fleetwood, where it runs along the main street as a classic tramway.

6   Under the provisions of the 1985 Transport Act the tramway is owned by the Borough Council but operated by the municipal company Blackpool Transport Services Ltd. There has been some bus competition, but since, during the summer months, demand for seafront transport outstrips supply, this has not reduced tramway traffic significantly. After a period of little change, eight new cars have joined the fleet of 80 trams, and a programme of track improvements carried out, with some financial assistance from Lancashire County Council. However investment in further modern rolling stock is an issue that the company must face. The demonstration of a Tatra tram from Czechoslovakia during 1990 may provide a pointer to the future.

TYNE & WEAR
7   Planned in the early 1970s as the essential part of an integrated passenger transport system for Newcastle and surrounding towns, the Tyne & Wear metro was designed to use existing British Rail tracks, with new tunnels to reach the city centre. Opened in 1980, it has grown to 56 route km with 44 stations carrying 47 million passengers annually. A further low cost 3.5-km extension to Newcastle Airport has been authorised and should be built by 1991, with some private finance. Studies continue on other possible extensions, including to Washington and Sunderland. With its fully segregated and signalled tracks the Metro is at the heavy end of the light rail spectrum.

Amsterdam tram

Lille Val

Toronto UTDC

Fig. 1. Amsterdam tram conventional light rail; Lille VAL automated guideway; Toronto UTDC automated light rail

8   The Metro is owned and operated by the Passenger
Transport Executive. Initially the implementation of the
1985 Transport Act led to the collapse of through ticketing
provision, and increased bus competition. The position has
now stabilised and some through ticketing with local bus
operators has been reintroduced.

LONDON

9   <u>Docklands Light Railway.</u> The initial 12 km system
promoted by the London Docklands Development Corporation
with central government finance opened for public service
in August 1987. Initially designed to carry 2 000
passengers/hr, the massive office developments on the Isle
of Dogs will require the 1.8 km city extension to Bank now
under construction (with private finance), more cars and
higher frequencies to carry up to 20 000 passengers/hr.
About 10.5 million passengers were carried in 1988, but
traffic doubled in the first year of operation.

10 Summer 1989 saw the authorisation of a 7.5 km surface
extension to Beckton (financed by LDDC from the capture of
increased land values), and consultation is in progress on
a cross-river link to Greenwich and Lewisham. New orders
will take the present fleet of 11 cars to 65 by 1992. The

LRT activity in UK: locations

Fig. 2.   LRT activity in the UK: locations

use of new elevated structures and old railway alignments has made possible a fully-segregated system with automatic train operation. The Docklands Light Railway is a wholly-owned subsidiary of London Regional Transport, a nationalised undertaking.

11 Other London schemes. In 1986 London Regional Transport and the Network South-East sector of British Rail published the report of a joint study of the possible scope for light rail elsewhere in London, identifying some 30 opportunities. As a result a major scheme for the Croydon area was chosen for detailed study by consultants to demonstrate possible applications and investigate practical possibilities. The scheme includes the conversion and extension of BR lines with new low-cost stations, plus a 2-km (approx) link across the centre of Croydon.

12 The report was published in 1988 and recommends that BR routes to Wimbledon (10 km) and Elmers End (3 km), a new 8-km line to New Addington and the central link should proceed. Consultation with the Borough Council has taken place, and the project reviewed in the light of separate South London transportation studies. A full engineering study will now take place to permit preparation of a Parliamentary Bill.

13 A study is in progress for a LRT system based around Kingston-upon-Thames (including existing rail lines), while a light rail link to the refurbished Alexandra Palace is being advocated by the Borough of Haringey.

MANCHESTER

14 Greater Manchester PTE are promoting a scheme for the construction in stages of a 100 km network of light rail lines based on existing BR tracks, but with 3 km of street running to link the existing peripheral railway stations with the city centre. The enabling Bills for the 32-km first phase linking Bury and Altrincham have been passed by Parliament and a government grant under Section 56 of the 1968 Transport Act approved . A contract for the design, construction, operation and maintenance of the first line was awarded to a consortium of companies in autumn 1989 and work is in progress to permit the Metrolink to open in 1991/2. The operating concession is for 15 years with assets remaining in PTE ownership.

15 Further extensions to serve the Salford Quays dockland redevelopment, the Trafford Park industrial estate and the proposed Dumplington retail centre are proposed with a Bills seeking authorisation before Parliament. These would be linked to the present Oldham and Rochdale rail line, with street running in the latter town.

PAPER 1

SOUTH YORKSHIRE

16 The South Yorkshire PTE deposited a Parliamentary
Bill in November 1985 for a 22 km light rail line across
Sheffield. The line is based on highway alignments, but
with about 50% segregation through the use of reserved
tracks. The Bill completed its passage through Parliament
in October 1988. A second Bill was deposited in November
1988 for a 7-km line to the Don Valley, a major
regeneration area and site for the World Student Games in
1991. This Bill received the Royal Assent in December 1989.
The goverment indicated approval in principle, subject to
further analysis and private sector involvement. In-mid
1989 tenders were invited for design and construction, and
separately for rolling stock, and for operation and
maintenance. The government has now stated that the scheme
meets the criteria for Section 56 grant, but no funding can
be made available for work to start in 1990.

AVON

17 A private company, Advanced Transport for Avon Ltd,
has produced plans for a regional light rail network based
on Bristol and deposited a Parliamentary Bill for the first
line (17 km wholly on existing or disused BR alignments
between Portishead and Wapping wharf) in November 1987.
This received Royal Assent in May 1989, after delay caused
by political controversey in Bristol. Bills for the
second stage (43 km), including street running through the
city centre, lines on former railway alignment to Yate and
alongside British Rail tracks to Filton and the highway to
Cribbs Causeway, were deposited in November 1989.

18 ATA is associated with property development
companies, and the proposed financing package includes
contributions from developers of land likely to enhance in
value with an adjacent rail transit service. However the
company also intends to seek Government Section 56 grant,
requiring a matching contribution from Avon County Council.
The Council also have to agree the highway operation
aspects of the proposals before further parliamentary
approvals can be secured. It is likely a joint venture
company will have to be formed with the County and City
Councils if this scheme is to succeed.

WEST MIDLANDS

19 In September 1987 the West Midlands PTE launched its
Midland Metro project for regional light rail system
covering Birmingham and the Black Country. Extensive
consultation took place with all interested parties,
including private developers and the European Regional
Development Fund for financing. A bill for the first line
(19 km, Birmingham-Wolverhampton) was deposited in November
1988, involving mostly disused BR alignments, but with some
street running at Wolverhampton. Royal Assent was received
in November 1989. Two further Bills were deposited in

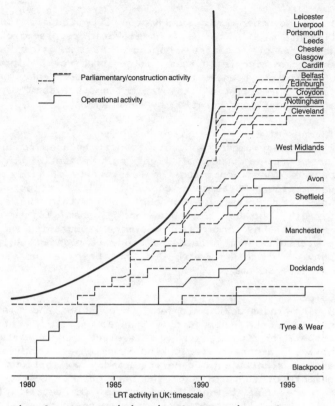

Fig. 3. LRT activity in the UK: timescale

November 1989, for lines from Birmingham to Castle Bromwich
and the National Exhibition Centre/Airport (26 km) and
between Wolverhampton, Walsall and Dudley (26 km). A subway
rather than a surface solution has been chosen for the
central Birmingham alignment. A route in Coventry is being
studied in preparation for a 1990 Bill submission.

WEST YORKSHIRE
20 The West Yorkshire PTE's development strategy for
public transport includes the reintroduction of
trolleybuses in Bradford and a 21 km street based (but 90%
reserved track) light rail system for Leeds, linking the
city centre with the eastern suburbs. Consultants worked up
details so that a Bill for the first line could be
deposited in Parliament in November 1988, but controversey
with Leeds City Council caused this to be withdrawn. The
City Council then undertook its own study for an automated
cross-city light rapid transit line (Seacroft - Middleton)
and carried out consultation with a view to submitting a
Bill to Parliament in November 1989. This project also
failed and a joint working party of the PTE and City
Council is now seeking an agreed strategy for the future.

11

PAPER 1

SOUTHAMPTON

21 In November 1988 Southampton City Council lodged a
Parliamentary Bill for a 4-km elevated people-mover line
around the city centre, hoping that the line can be
financed by contributions from commercial interests
involved in city centre retailing and development. The plan
envisages an automated light rapid transit system. The Bill
is still under consideration by Parliament..

SOUTH HAMPSHIRE

22 In 1988 Hampshire County Council engaged consultants
to carry out a study of light rail potential in South
Hampshire. They identified the feasibility of lines in the
Fareham-Gosport-Portsmouth corridor (11.2 km including a
tunnel under Portsmouth Harbour), and within the city of
Portsmouth between Southsea and Cosham (8 km). The
appraisal of the former line was more favourable, and after
local consultation, a detailed study is planned. A private
company, South Hants Metro Ltd, has been set up, and may
promote the scheme.

TEESSIDE

23 The Teesside Development Corporation and Cleveland
County Council have jointly funded a study into the
potential for light rail in Cleveland. Consultants have
identified a core route linking Stockton and Middlesbrough
offering significant benefits and two options (new
alignments or conversion of the Darlington - Saltburn rail
line) are now being worked up in detail. Public
consultation will precede Bill submission in November.

NOTTINGHAM

24 In 1989 Nottingham Development Enterprise, backed by
city and county councils, commissioned a feasibility study
into a possible light rail system in the greater
Nottingham area. This identified a 12-km north-south line
linking Hucknall with the city centre and Midland station
as an initial route for consultation, with other routes
considered suitable to form a network. Further work is in
progress to identify the best city centre alignment prior
to submission of a Bill in November.

EDINBURGH

25 After a two-year study of public transport options,
including widespread public consultation, in mid-1989
Lothian Regional Council announced plans for a light rail
system with an 18-km north - south line
(Muirhouse/Davidsons Mains - Kaimes/Gilmerton via a city
centre subway including in part an abandoned rail tunnel)
as the first phase, with a target date of 1996. After
public consultation, a Bill may be submitted in November. A
second, east - west, line would link Leith and Wester
Hailes.

12

GLASGOW

26 Strathclyde Passenger Transport Executive have carried out a two-year Public Transport Development Study which included investigation of the potential for light rail transit. The study reported at the end of 1989 and identifies options for fully and partially segregated light rail. Public consultation is being evaluated.

DUNDEE

27 The City Centre Initiative of Tayside Regional Council and Dundee City Council includes a study for a light rapid transit link between city centre shopping areas and a redevelopment area. An automated people mover system is envisaged.

LIVERPOOL

28 The Merseyside Development Corporation is investigating ways of regenerating the older docks area and has identified the potential for light rail over the route of the former Overhead Railway between Sandhills and the former Garden Festival site. The Passenger Transport Executive is understood to be examining light rail potential for routes to the eastern suburbs.

BELFAST

29 Northern Ireland Railways has put forward a plan for light rail development, including conversion of its line to Bangor, and a detailed study is being carried out by Queens University.

READING

30 A County Council study of rail potential in central Berkshire identified possible light rail opportunities in Reading's Bath Rd and Basingstoke Rd corridors. It is hoped to carry out a more detailed study in 1990.

SWINDON

31 In 1989 Wiltshire County Council commissioned consultants for a transportation study that includes examination of the potential for light rail in the Swindon area. This concluded that heavy rail options were unlikely to be economic but there were opportunities for a viable light rail system as an alternative to wholly road-based solutions.

CHESTER

32 A pre-feasibility study sponsored by County and City Councils examined the potential for light rail in Chester and reported favourably on two corridors geared to the potential for park-and-ride to alleviate growing congestion in the historic centre. A full-scale feasibility study is expected to report in 1990.

TAPLIN

CARDIFF
33 Consultants retained by the Cardiff Bay Development Corporation have proposed a light rail link from the city centre and Central Station to the Cardiff Docks redevelopment area, and this has won the support of South Glamorgan County Council for a full study, as predicted traffic levels in the area seem likely to strain the highway network. A Bill may be submitted in November 1991.

CAMBRIDGE
34 The preparation of a new Cambridge Master Plan by the County Council includes detailed assessment of light rail proposals using existing or abandoned railway alignments, with a link to the city centre.

NORWICH
35 A major transportation study now in progress includes in its brief the examination of light rail options.

GREAT YARMOUTH
36 A privately-sponsored 2.5-km light rapid transit line as a tourist attraction and park-and-ride link appears to be supported by the Borough Council.

BASILDON
37 The Borough Council have proposed an overhead people-mover type system for a 5-km link between the railway station and new Astrodome complex.

SOUTHEND-ON-SEA
38 Essex County Council are carrying out a general transportation study to examine future options, including possibilities for light rail.

CHELMSFORD
39 The Chamber of Commerce has proposed a town centre peoplemover on a circular route linking rail station, car parks and shopping centre.

COLNE VALLEY
40 Plans by a local pressure group for light rail in the corridor of the London Underground Chesham-Watford and British Rail Watford-St Albans lines have been taken up for consideration by Hertfordshire County Council.

LUTON
41 Bus operator Luton & District have produced plans for a light rail line linking Luton and Dunstable.

BEDFORD
42 The Bedford Area Passenger Transport Study has raised the possibility of a further study of light rail options.

MILTON KEYNES

43 A private report has been produced advocating the feasibility of a two-line light rail system.

LEICESTER

44 Proposals for a north-south line, using abandoned railway alignment with street running in the centre, have been prepared by the County Council as part of an overall transportation strategy. A full feasibility study is expected.

STOKE-ON-TRENT/POTTERIES

45 An officer working party of County, City and Borough Councils is giving consideration to investigation of the potential for light rail.

HULL

46 Humberside County Council and the City Council have commissioned consultants to examine options for various forms of light rapid transit.

PRESTON

47 A private consultant has undertaken preliminary investigation into light rail for a park-and-ride link.

MEDWAY TOWNS

48 Kent County Council and the District Council are discussing a possible joint venture study of light rail.

BRIGHTON

49 Preliminary consideration has been given to light rail with consultants producing a proposal for a Patcham - town centre - Seafront line. A detailed feasibility study may follow in 1990.

GUILDFORD

50 A feasibility study of alternative transport provision commissioned in 1990 will include consideration of light rail options.

PLYMOUTH

51 Consultants have recommended that light rail be examined as an option in the redevelopment of the waterside area of the city. The City and County Councils are considering whether to pursue formal studies.

EXETER

52 An internal study by the County Council has not resulted in any recommendation for more detailed study.

GLOUCESTER/CHELTENHAM

53 Gloucesteshire County Council are commissioning a pre-feasibility study for light rail in a north-south corridor.

GLOUCESTER

54 The City tourist plan includes a street-based tramway link between the city centre and the redevelopment site at the historic Gloucester docks. Detailed consultation is in progress with developers who may provide financing opportunities. This will be an example of the heritage tramway concept that is proving successful in the USA (either free-standing or in association with a light rail scheme).

SWANSEA

55 A report commissioned by South Wales Transport has identified options for reopening the Swansea and Mumbles tramway as a tourist and transport attraction. However this seems not to have won local authority endorsement.

PRIVATE SYSTEMS

56 Light transit also embraces a number of private systems that at present serve either airports or amusement parks. Gatwick Airport features two examples of the Westinghouse guideway, while Birmingham Airport is linked to the International rail station by the unique Maglev system. A Westinghouse shuttle is being incorporated in the new terminal arrangements at Stanstead airport. Amusement or pleasure facilities such as Blackpool Pleasure Beach, Alton Towers and Beaulieu feature monorails. Another is about to be opened linking Merry Hill shopping complex at Dudley with car parking and retail areas.

57 Such systems are usually patented and linked to proprietory interests which promote them as solutions to urban transport problems. They may have limited scope as shuttles or distributors (for instance a monorail features in proposals for central Birmingham redevelopment, and other systems have been referred to above under Southampton, Dundee, Chelmsford, Basildon and Great Yarmouth). Their potential to deal with cross-city flows in a cost-effective way remains to be proven, given the economics of overseas examples such as VAL in Lille and the Sydney monorail.

FURTHER POTENTIAL

58 It is clear from the number of schemes now under investigation that the potential for light transit has moved beyond the major conurbations. It is seen to have the flexibility to fit into a wide variety of urban situations, attract more patronage than buses, be capable of cost-effective implementation, and make a significant contribution towards urban regeneration and the protection of the environment. Its ability to influence the modal split in favour of public transport is seen as a key to relieving traffic congestion. In these circumstances many medium-size cities with traffic problems that cannot be

solved by road-based solutions, or with areas earmarked for regeneration, may find investigation of light rail solutions worthwhile.

59 Careful and financial economic assessment must go hand in hand with the alignment and engineering studies to make a valid case for serious consideration. The construction of further new schemes, which will make a call on scarce financial resources in both the public and private sectors, will depend very much on the financial case that can be made for their implementation. An agreed method of assessing the benefits to the community of social and environmental factors needs to be developed for inclusion in these studies. It will also be necessary to streamline the Parliamentary Private Bill process if the necessary legislation is to proceed to a timescale matching the aspirations of the promoting authorities (see chart). In Great Britain transport is a political issue, and the professionals may not always have the last word.

REFERENCES
1   Modern Tramway, LRTA, 1980-90
2   Local Transport Today, LTT, 1989-90
3   Ed SKELSEY G. B. Light Rail '87, LRTA, 1987
4   Provisional Guidance Note for LRT, DTp, 1989
5   Light Rail Trends, UITP, 1989
6   Light Rail Transit, PTE Group, 1988
7   Light Rail for London, London Transport, 1986
8   HURDLE D. Light Rail: some implications for the
         South-East, SERPLAN, 1988
9   Ed TAPLIN M. R. Light Rail Review, LRTA, 1989

2. Light transit to combat congestion

E. JOOS, Verkehrsbetriebe Zurich

Introduction

This paper on 'the Zurich Model' shows the potential in the existing streets of historic cities to arrange fast, regular and reliable public transport. The Zurich Model helps to ease congestion by redistributing road areas, giving more space for short-range public passenger transport and pedestrians and less for private motoring. The objective of the traffic policy, devised after several referenda on public works by the citizens of Zurich, was to guarantee the accessibility of the city centre for employees and visitors in an attractive and inexpensive way.

Today, traffic engineers speak of urban traffic management as a new challenge, but this is exactly what Zurich has undergone over the last 15 years: not increasing the road area or building new works for traffic, but organizing the existing road space and managing urban traffic with clear objectives. A comparison of some European cities shows that the population in the area covered by Zurich's transport authority (VBZ) uses trams and buses nearly twice as much as the populations of most of the other cities. This shows that the urban traffic management has been extremely successful with regard to modal split and therefore to environmental improvement.

Table 1. Population and Trips Per Annum in European Cities

	Population in transport area: millions	Trips per annum: millions	Trips per person per annum in transport area
London	6.7	1941	290
Vienna	1.52	603	397
Amsterdam	0.68	220	320
Stockholm	1.5	432	288
Dusseldorf	1.1	170	160
Hannover	0.54	124	230
Cologne	1.1	170	150
Stuttgart	0.56	139	250
Greater Manchester	2.6	341	131
Tyne and Wear	1.1	374	340
West Midlands	2.6	343	170
Zurich	0.55	259	470

Light transit systems. Thomas Telford, London, 1990

Political considerations

Referenda in Zurich not only rejected new street or parking projects, but also two large-scale projects to solve the public short-range transport problem by putting public transport underground. These were the Tiefbahn tram subway project of 1962 that, at the time, would have cost £200 million, and the 1973 U-Bahn project that would have cost more than £375 million. The city council of Zurich saw the double rejection of this type of project as a mandate to continue to restrict public transport to the existing trams, trolleybuses and motor buses, but at the same time to develop these means of transport into an efficient and modern transport system.

At a political level, willingness to encourage public transport grew during the intensive dates that preceded the referenda on the large-scale projects. The support of public transport by both advocates and opponents meant that action simply had to follow.

In June 1973, a public campaign was launched with the objective of making £75 million available for projects to speed up public transport. In March 1977 this initiative was backed by a referendum. On the one hand, funds were then available to carry out plans to speed up traffic and on the other, even more importantly, a majority of the population concerned expressly agreed to a transport policy favouring trams and buses.

In August 1975, a parliamentary resolution required the Zurich city council to issue a policy guideline to its departments, indicating that public transport should generally be encouraged, taking account of the needs of both pedestrians and the environment. Accordingly the city council issued the following policy statement:

'In accordance with the city council's repeatedly stated wish to give priority to public transport when weighing up various transport interests, the city departments are hereby instructed in principle to give preferential treatment to public transport. Moreover, reasonable provision must be made for the needs of pedestrians, disabled people, cyclists and delivery vehicles. The environment, the quality of life in the city's residential areas and the townscape must also be taken into account'.

Organising the traffic speed-up programmes

Even if an underground line had been built, large parts of the tram and bus system would have remained above ground. In view of this, the city planning office in July 1971 published a study entitled 'Tram route 10: journey time measurements, and measures to increase its speed'. The study comprised more than 60 timed trips, using a stopwatch and a report pad. Over 200 causes of delay at 152 locations were recorded, together

Fig. 1.   Trams, trolley- and motor buses: a modern transport
system for Zurich. This view of Bahnhofplatz
demonstrates the intermodal interchange with the S-
Bahn System (heavy rail), using all the same tickets
and fares.

Fig. 2.   The data-controlled operational control system is an
irreplaceable traffic regulation tool. For each tram
and bus it knows at any time where it should be and
the actual position. The difference - lateness or
earliness - is shown to the driver and traffic
controller.

with type and duration. The result was an initial speed-up
programme consisting of 105 individual remedial measures.
These included traffic islands and boundary elements (e.g.
kerbstones), left-turn junction restrictions, no-waiting areas
and the introduction of traffic lights with control systems
that favoured trams.

Debate on how these measures could be carried out show the
need for interdisciplinary collaboration and, on the
suggestion of the city Police Commissioner (one of the nine
elected members of the city council, the Executive), two new
bodies were formed. These were the executive council to
promote public transport, responsible for guidelines and
decision-making, and a working party for the development of
projects and for project management. The city council
resolved in March 1973 that `A special organization will be
formed under the Police Commissioner with the task of
establishing priority for public transport based on a tram and
bus network'.

The members of the executive council are the three directly-
concerned executive city councillors: the Police Commissioner,
the Chairman of Building Works and City Planning, and the
Chairman of the Industrial Department (VBZ); together with
such relevant senior officers as the head of the traffic
police, the City Engineer, the City Planner and the Director
of the VBZ. Both the executive council and the working party
meet every four to six weeks. The working party develops
projects ready for introduction or suggests concrete measures
for traffic policing, while the executive council issues
guidelines and considers proposals made by the working party.
Executive council recommendations are generally accepted by
the city council because of the involvement of the three
councillors concerned. Traffic speed-up projects costing
more than £400 000 have to be approved by the city parliament;
if they cost more than £400 million, they must be put to a
referendum.

Nature and scope of traffic speed-up measures

Both the study on tram route 10 and later analyses based on
statistical data collected by the operational control centre
clearly showed three main causes of delay:

(1)   delays such as vehicles turning left or vehicles forced
        by parked cars to drive along the track

(2)   delays often of up to 60 seconds caused by
        conventionally controlled traffic lights

(3)   delays caused by collision, sometimes harmless ones,
        that block the road and the track and seriously affected
        the regularity of whole routes.

Together, all these delays made passengers feel that public transport was slow and unreliable. The objective was therefore to make the Zuri-Linie fast and reliable again. The speed-up programme concentrated on three separate objectives, and each of these will be discussed in detail:

(1)   unhindered trips between junctions, without hold-ups caused by private traffic, to be achieved by building special lines and separate bus lanes

(2)   'zero' waiting time for public transport vehicles at light-controlled junctions, by developing a fully flexible control philosophy

(3)   extension of the data-controlled operational control system, so that the operational control centre is always informed about deviations from the timetable and other programmes, and can remedy the situation or help by putting previously-designed measures into effect.

Unhindered trips between junctions

Measures under this heading were to ensure that trams and buses overtake slow moving or jammed lines of private traffic, rapidly reaching the next junction so that the priorities there could take effect. Moreover it was important to prevent trams or buses from being forced to brake to stop due to obstruction by cars turning left or from cars themselves avoiding parked cars. In Zurich we generally had to carry out these improvements within the available road space, for example, by transforming an entire stretch of road into a pedestrian and public transport area, by prohibiting parking along the route, or by redesigning the road and introducing separate tram lanes. Because of the rules governing approval of projects according to cost, the rebuilding plans generally had to be put before the city's parliament, and again and again political support for the scheme was confirmed. In the last 15 years, the following measures have been carried out to this end:

(1)   prohibition of parking and waiting on 15 lengths of road
(2)   12 no-left-turns in roads used by trams
(3)   28 no-left-turns at junctions with roads used by trams
(4)   65 no-priority zones at junctions with roads used by trams or buses
(5)   16 kilometres of bus lane
(6)   around 36 construction projects costing up to £4 million, such as stop islands, separate tram lanes, pedestrian zones with tram or bus services, multi-track areas, bus lanes, etc.
(7)   2 new stretches of tram route, 2 and 6.4 km long respectively, with their own tram lanes throughout.

Fig. 3.   Redistribution of the street surface area in favour
          of trams and buses so they can speed past slow or
          stationery lines of other traffic.   Zurich introduced
          16 km of bus lanes (above) and 90% of the present 62
          km of the double track for trams.   The segregated
          tram track with grass (below) halves the noise.

The cost of these measures - excluding the tramway
extensions - was around £40 million. During each project, a
firm distinction was made between speed-up costs and normal
maintenance costs, including conduits and work lines.
The presence of sufficient uniformed police was ensured to
enforce the prohibitions and directions affecting traffic.
The officers were instructed to give preferential treatment to
public transport. The necessary supervision of the
arrangements increased the staff costs in the city police
force's annual budget.

Public transport preference at traffic lights

The city of Zurich adopted its own way of attaining the
maximum preferential treatment at traffic lights. Thanks to
the guidelines issued by the executive council, it was taken
for granted that the city police, as the authority responsible
for traffic lights, would tackle this problem themselves. On
the principle that trams and buses do not require a green
phase for long, but they do need it when they approach a
junction and, with the help of computers, the police developed
a practically perfect public transport orientated control
scheme for traffic lights. Today, out of a total of 363
traffic light installations, 270 are crossed by tram or bus
routes. Of these, 217 respond to trams and buses. In fact,
they respond to small transmitters in the vehicles and
induction loops embedded in the road surface.

The system that controls traffic lights is completely
independent from the operational control system. Every tram
or bus benefits, regardless of whether it is on schedule. The
effects of this control scheme can be summarized as follows.

(1)   Trams and buses are allowed to proceed only when they
        really need to, but they do so without delay.

(2)   If a public transport vehicle crosses several traffic
        lights, the traffic computer normally activates a
        synchronized green zone for it.

(3)   If there are light signals immediately after a stop, the
        tram or bus signals its presence as it approaches them.
        The lights change to `go' after 10 - 15 seconds and
        remain at `go' until the vehicle signals that it has
        passed. At termini and interchange points - where
        waiting times vary - the driver signals the vehicle's
        presence when he operates the door lock switch.

(4)   Generally, even though priority is clearly given to
        public transport, the same volume of private traffic as
        before can be accommodated. Traffic jams are prevented
        by avoiding unnecessary green phases and systematically
        monitoring congestion areas.

Fig. 4.   Trams and buses require no lengthy green periods in
          the traffic-light cycle, but they need a green phase
          quickly when they do arrive. Because trams and buses
          arrive very irregularly, traffic lights cannot be
          controlled with regular cycles. The 18 traffic
          computers generated on a line, with the information
          of over 2000 SESAM detectors (below), which respond
          to trams, buses and private vehicles, co-ordinated
          programmes, with the objectives of security, minimal
          congestion and no waiting time for trams and buses.

(5)   Private motorists and pedestrians also benefit from this
       'need-controlled' fully flexible signal technology.

Zurich's computerized traffic signal system consists of 18
traffic computers working in pairs and some 2000 detectors
embedded in the road. These monitor trams, buses, congestion
areas and pedestrians. All this and the necessary software
costs about £1.5 million on depreciation, interest payments,
programme serving and staff. The storage needs and software
expenses associated with this practically perfect control
technology are about five times as high as for a normal,
modern, computerized traffic light control system.

The operational control system

The operational control system is an irreplaceable help to
manage the operation of trams and buses. Since the computer
in the operational control centre knows both the timetable and
the actual position of each individual vehicle at any time, it
continually tells each driver whether he is on schedule. He
can therefore check his own progress. This substantially
improves observance of timetables and therefore regularity as
well.

The operational control system permits efficient problem
management. The traffic controller can see delays as they
build up on individual routes. He has in reserve two trams
and five buses, all with drivers and positioned at strategic
points in the network and waiting for orders. Ideally, he can
add an extra vehicle into service to run to the timetable that
a delayed vehicle should have observed taking the pressure off
it and helping it to recover from the delay. Alternatively,
he might take other steps designed to bring the timetable back
into line as soon as possible. If accidents, processions,
demonstrations, etc. block a route, the operational control
centre will order diversions and, if necessary, have buses
take over tram routes. As needed, police, ambulance and
technical services can be ordered straight to the spot. The
purpose of all these measures is to deal with the problem as
soon as possible and to limit its effects so that as few
people as possible suffer. It is also important to keep
passengers in the vehicles of the Zuri-Linie and at important
stops, informed through loudspeakers connected to the
operational control centre.

In order to maintain uninterrupted tram services during
route blockages and authorized processions, we have a
reasonable number of reserve routes by using branch-offs,
diversion tracks and turning loops. The operational control
is flexible and can even direct trams.

A variety of statistical data can be collected with the help
of the system's automatic location monitoring. These can
quantify weaknesses in the network and provide a basis for
proposals for improvement.

If we bought the whole system new today it would cost around £6 million. The annual costs of depreciation, interest, software servicing, staff, etc. come to about £1.2 million.

Cost-benefit considerations

For less than £100 million investment or less than £10 million on annual costs for depreciation, interest and operating costs, the whole VBZ tram and bus network has been brought up to the highest standards of speed, regularity and

Table 2. Cost-benefit comparison between roads and public transport

Cost : Transport corridor of 1 km length in £ millions Benefit: Capacity in persons per hour in one direction			
	Cost	Benefit	Cost/ benefit
Expressway (6-lanes)	30	5600	5300
Metro (heavy rail)	28	30000	900
Tramway, exclusive right of way	4.5	8000	600

Cost/benefit ratio for a metro is six times, and for tramways with exclusive right of way nearly ten times, better than for expressways.

Table 3. Cost-benefit comparison between expressway, heavy rail and bus and tram speed-up programmes

Cost : Expressway network (not yet completed), S-Bahn (heavy rail) system and speed-up programmes for trams and buses in Zurich, in £ millions Benefit: Capacity in persons per hour in one direction			
	Cost	Benefit	Cost/ Benefit
Expressway network, without ring expressway in Zurich	750	15000	50000
S-Bahn Zurich	550	50000	11000
Speed-up programmes for trams and buses in Zurich	100	40000	2500

In Zurich the cost/benefit ratio for speed-up programmes for trams and buses is 20 times better than for the expressway network. For the S-Bahn system (heavy rail) it is still four times better.

Table 4. Cost-benefit figures for Metro, light rail and tram and bus transport

Cost	: Investments in transit-systems since 1960, in £ millions				
Benefit	: Fast, regular, reliable transit				
Cost/benefit:	In £ per trip and £ per inhabitant				
	Investments in £ millions	Trips per annum, in millions	Inhabitants in transport area, in millions	£ per trip	£ per inhabitant
Metro					
Munich	1100	361	1.4	3.0	790
Stockholm	1500	432	1.5	3.5	1000
Vienna	1000	603	1.5	1.7	670
Light rail transit					
Dusseldorf	700	170	1.1	4.1	640
Hannover	600	124	540000	4.8	1110
Cologne	500	170	1.1	2.9	450
Stuttgart	500	139	560000	3.6	890
Tram and bus					
Zurich	100	259	550000	0.4	180

reliability. Successes of this sort are otherwise possible only if one builds an underground system, which involves much higher capital expenditure. Moreover, underground rail systems must be served by additional bus routes, and some of them also come to the surface somewhere, and both factors necessitate additional appropriate speed-up programmes. Cost-benefit comparisons of different traffic policies are problematic. The benefit of the environment cannot be expressed in figures, and aspects of quality for users and the persons concerned with pollution and noise cannot be accurately quantified either. I will try to make clear the complex problem looking from different points of view (Tables 2 - 4).

20 years ago, the eight cities compared had the same preconditions: historic city core, increasing concentration of employment in the CBD, private motoring reaching its limits of increase, and an existing, efficient tram system. All these cities realized an efficient and attractive short-range public passenger transport system. The three biggest - Munich, Stockholm and Vienna - did it with metro systems. Metro systems here have been unavoidable because of the high link volumes. Four cities solved their problems by building light rail transit systems. The capacity is about the same, but in the CBD they operate in tunnels, making the city streets free for private motoring or pedestrianization. Zurich remained true to the 'old-fashioned' trams, developed into a modern LRT by giving it priority with space and green phases on traffic lights. The same was also done for buses.

Even knowing the problematic nature of this comparison, it is evident, that the Zurich Model has an excellent cost/

benefit ratio: in terms of trips it is 4 to 11 times better, and in terms of population it is 2 to 6 times better than those of the other cities.

Benefit to the quality of the environment

Every kind of transport exposes people to some kind of harmful emissions. These emissions must of course be minimized. As more people travel in fewer, larger vehicles (the buses, trams or trains of short-range public transport) the danger of accidents, the amount of road congestion and of harmful emissions decreases. Thus the quality of the environment and therefore the attractiveness of the city as a place to live, work and to spend leisure time improves. Less private motoring also means

(1)   safer traffic, less risk to children and elderly people

(2)   less noise in residential areas and on main roads

(3)   streets and squares can serve better as meeting places and playgrounds with less traffic

(4)   less pollution and therefore better public health.

Too many cars
inhospitable city

Vicious
circle

Even more cars,
inhospitable city

Jammed roads
lack of parking

New and bigger
roads, building
of parking space

Redistribution of road areas: more space for public shortrange passenger transport and pedestrians - less space for private motoring

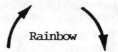

Rainbow

Too many cars,
inhospitable city

More urbanity,
more economic strength,
less/stabilized
private traffic

Fig. 5.   Summary of why Zurich's transport policy works.

Conclusions

The Zurich model is based on outstanding high-tech innovation. Both the computer-controlled traffic lights that give priority to trams and buses and the data-controlled operational control centre are state-of-the-art achievements in their fields. However, the model is also based on functional organization. This came into being with the executive council and the working party for the development of public transport, and a firm orientation towards the objective in mind. Decisive for the model's success was the political will to make public transport fast, regular and reliable

(1)   with little money (and few building sites)

(2)   without enlarging road space

(3)   while accepting perceptible restrictions on private motoring.

The people of Zurich are said to be good businessmen and tend to adopt pragmatic solutions. Without being in any way spectacular, Zurich has managed to break out of the vicious circle of traffic policy and turn it into a rainbow (Fig. 5).

This has undoubtedly led to increased economic strength. The city set clear limits on the encroachment caused by private motoring, and redistributed traffic areas in favour of short-range public passenger transport and pedestrians rather than to the car, and the economic power of the city has not been adversely affected. Indeed, it has benefited from its transport system more than other cities that follow a less consistent transport policy. The proportion of city traffic represented by private cars is only half as large in Zurich as in most other cities in Western Europe. Nevertheless

(1)   land prices in Zurich - a measure of net product created per unit of area - are among the world's highest

(2)   Switzerland has one of the world's highest gross domestic products, a substantial portion of which is created in Zurich

(3)   the citizens of Zurich pay 30% of their gross domestic product to the state in the form of taxes and social security payments - citizens in the UK and in most other countries in Europe (where traffic policy is paid for out of taxes) pay around 40% or more.

To sum up, the route to city traffic with reduced energy consumption, lower noise levels and less air pollution lies in improving the system of trams and buses on the streets. Urban traffic management based on the redistribution of the use of the surface area of roads and of the green-light phase on traffic lights in favour of trams, buses and pedestrians is not merely the objective of a traffic policy, but is a strong economic objective.

3. Light transit to stimulate development: the London Docklands experience

B. T. COLLINS, London Docklands Development Corporation

SYNOPSIS.   This paper examines the interrelationship between the Docklands Light Railway and the regeneration of the London Docklands and suggests some tentative conclusions that may be applicable elsewhere in British Cities.

LONDON DOCKLANDS DEVELOPMENT CORPORATION

1.   The London Docklands Development Corporation, an Urban Development Corporation, was set up in 1981 to secure the regeneration of the 2,226 hectares of the London Docklands (the UDA), 83% of which lies north of the Thames.

2.   On the north side of the River Thames the Corporation's area stretches from Tower Bridge 10.5 kilometres eastwards to the line of the proposed East London River Crossing at Beckton and encompasses St Katharine's Docks, Limehouse Basin, the Isle of Dogs, the Royal Docks and Beckton.   South of the River the area runs from London Bridge 4 kilometres eastwards to the edge of Deptford (Lewisham) and includes St. Saviour's Dock and the remains of the Surrey Docks.

3.   The Corporation is a limited life Quango sponsored by the Department of the Environment currently funded by a combination of annual Government Grant and land sales.   Unlike the great majority of commercial and public bodies it cannot borrow – this makes managing its cash flow very complex when individual projects may represent more than one year's Grant and land sale income is subject to market fluctuations.

4.   It has a duty to acquire derelict and polluted land and, using both private and public funds, ensure the redevelopment of that and other land in its area so as to ensure the lasting regeneration of the Docklands.   This has included the provision of major sewerage works, highways, the Docklands Light Railway, large scale private and housing association development as well as the refurbishment of Council owned dwellings, major shopping, community, education, job training and leisure facilities and the financial support of community activities.

5.   The Corporation is neither a Highway nor a Transport
Authority but it is responsible for Development Control and
has Compulsory Purchase powers.

6.   When the Corporation was formed in 1981 the population of
the Area was less than 40,000 and the number of jobs was down
to 27,200 and continuing to fall.   By 2001 it is expected that
the population will be about 100,000 and that there will more
than 200,000 jobs.

7.   In 1981 a high proportion of the Corporation's area was
derelict and much of the remainder was underused or run down.
The Docklands communities tended to regard themselves as being
isolated and abandoned as seemingly post-war prosperity had
passed them by.

GETTING REGENERATION STARTED
8.   The problems facing the Corporation in 1981 were very
great.   The UDA suffered from the corollary of nothing
succeeding like success which is that nothing fails like
failure; and the Docklands undoubtedly felt like a failed
area.

9.   East London had acute transport problems before 1981,
aggravated by the lack of river crossings.   Access to the
Docklands on both sides of the Thames was particularly
difficult both for public and private transport.

10.   The Isle of Dogs – which features so prominently on the
aerial view at the start of every East Enders episode – was
isolated on three sides by the Thames and on the fourth by
West India Docks.   There were no rail services operational and
even the bus services were regarded as being outstandingly
poor.   One of the most used roads giving access to the Isle of
Dogs is aptly named 'Narrow Street'.

11.   The Royal Docks is served by only one rail line which,
unusually and almost perversely, does not connect direct to
central London but sweeps instead around north and west London
to Richmond.   Surrey Docks on the south side of the Thames is
in a peninsular void of British Rail lines but with what was
in 1981 a poor relation of an underground line.

12.   The A13, a west to east trunk road from the City of
London toward Southend, running on the north boundary of the
UDA parallel to the Thames, was (and still is) hopelessly
overloaded as are all parallel routes and rat runs.   Unlike
west London, nothing like the A4/M4 and A40/M40 have been
constructed in east London.

13.   It was clear that improving the road and rail
transportation systems serving the London Docklands was one of
the most important requirements for successful regeneration.

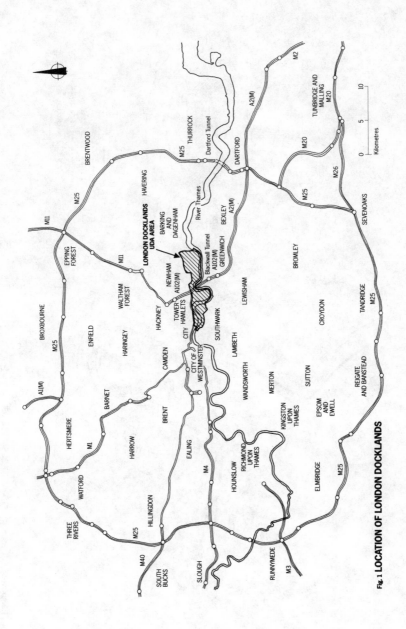

Fig. 1 LOCATION OF LONDON DOCKLANDS

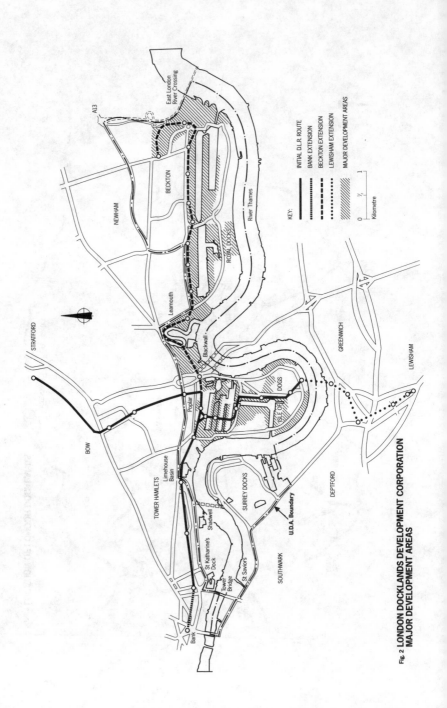

**Fig. 2 LONDON DOCKLANDS DEVELOPMENT CORPORATION
MAJOR DEVELOPMENT AREAS**

KEY:

INITIAL D.L.R. ROUTE

BANK EXTENSION

BECKTON EXTENSION

LEWISHAM EXTENSION

MAJOR DEVELOPMENT AREAS

0   ½   1
Kilometre

It has also turned out to be by far the most expensive
activity that the Corporation has and will be undertaking. By
the time the Corporation is wound up it is likely to have
incurred about £1,000 million on transport improvements.

Fig. 3. The Isle of Dogs before regeneration started

14.   Whilst initial redevelopment in Surrey Docks and to the
north of the Royal Docks concentrated on housing activities it
was concluded that in the west of the UDA (Wapping and
Limehouse) and in the Isle of Dogs (part of which had
Enterprise Zone status) the market would support a mixture of
relatively high density, predominantly private, housing and
commercial development.

15.   A light rail system, the Dockland Light Railway (DLR),
for the Wapping, Limehouse and Isle of Dogs areas was seen by
the Corporation as not only an effective way of providing
public transport but as a means of convincing developers that
the Corporation meant business and that private funds on a
large scale could safely be invested. After many travails
these objectives are being achieved.

16.   In the Wapping, Limehouse and Isle of Dogs areas already
some 4,500 dwellings have been provided and a further 2,000
are under construction. On the Isle of Dogs very high quality
commercial development at plot ratios of 7:1 is under
construction and land values have increased from less than
£50,000 an acre to a peak of £5 million an acre. Overall in
the UDA the leverage ratio of private to Corporation

Fig. 4.   The Isle of Dogs - higher density private dwellings

investment since 1981 has been 12:1.   Perhaps most significant
of all, market surveys show that the pre-1981 inhabitants
regard the DLR as being the most valuable improvement that has
been carried out by the Corporation.

DOCKLANDS LIGHT RAILWAY - INITIAL RAILWAY
   17. When the Corporation first conceived the Light Transit
system it was regarded in official circles with great
scepticism. It was felt that buses would do.   On normal
planning conceptions then current, they would have been
sufficient to carry projected public transport passengers.   It
required great courage and confidence to produce figures of
development growth and passengers to justify the £77 million
investment in the 12 Km required for the initial DLR.   Indeed
it has been suggested that it needed an ability to manipulate
figures in an imaginative way to produce the necessary
justification!

   18.   Half the cost of this initial railway has been borne by
London Regional Transport (LRT) and half by the Corporation.

   19.   Royal Assent to the act authorising the DLR multiplied
the enquiries about development opportunities some 10 fold.
The physical start on the construction of the DLR in the
mid-80's had the effect of stimulating development immediately
and as the railway took shape so development proposals became

Fig. 5.   The Isle of Dogs - lower density dockside private
          housing

more ambitious and more and more projects started.   By the
time the DLR opened in mid-1987 the 12.5 million sq ft Canary
Wharf development in the Isle of Dogs Enterprise Zone had
become firm and within a further year a total of 25 million sq
ft of development had either been completed, started or had
reached the stage of firm proposals.

20.   The Corporation is a regeneration agency and its
concerns go far beyond the physical redevelopment of the UDA.
The success of the redevelopment, north of the Thames
partially triggered by the DLR and partially by the tax
advantages of the Enterprise Zone, has enabled the Corporation
to encourage developers to augment its own job training and
community support activities by substantial similar efforts on
their own part.   This is continuing.

21.   By the time the DLR opened in 1987 it was clear that
contrary to initial design expectations it would soon be in
need of more than the 2,000 persons per hour one way crammed
capacity (4,000 in the Isle of Dogs) that the initial 11 No
cars of the initial fleet could provide.   Immediately LRT
began works to double the platform lengths so as to enable
two-car trains to be run and commenced an underground
extension to Bank Station on the Circle Underground system.

22.   Of the £180 million cost of these upgradings some 40% is
being borne by the Canadian Canary Wharf developer, Olympia &
York and the remainder by LRT.   The developer is also paying

Fig. 6. The Isle of Dogs – early commercial development
encouraged by prospect of the DLR

for a very high quality, and therefore expensive, new station
on the initial railway to serve his development.

23. The anticipated build up of employment is now so great
that it is proposed to relieve the DLR by a new underground
line – the Jubilee Line Extension. At the time of preparing
this paper it is being reported in the financial press that
the Department of Transport is having difficulty in obtaining
enough financial support from developers for funding the
capital cost of this extension. This may well be because most
developers believe the DLR will be sufficient and do not
realise how beneficial, by the mid-1990's, will be the Jubilee
Line Extension. No doubt some see a contribution as being
similar to a voluntary tax and anyway by the time the
underground line is open many developers will have disposed of
their interests.

DOCKLANDS LIGHT RAILWAY – BECKTON EXTENSION
24. The initial DLR served the Enterprise Zone of the Isle
of Dogs and the existing built up areas of Shadwell,
Limehouse, Poplar, Bromley and Bow in the London Borough of
Tower Hamlets as well as Stratford in the London Borough of
Newham. It does not serve the eastern half of the UDA in
Blackwall, Leamouth and the Royal Docks.

Fig. 7.   The Isle of Dogs 1989 - 12.5 million sq ft of Canary
          Wharf development encouraged by the DLR

25.   Whilst some 4,000 dwellings had been constructed to the
north of the Royal Docks by the autumn of 1989, relatively
little commercial development had taken place in areas not
provided with a Light Transit system.   Before the initial
railway had been opened in 1987 it had been concluded that an
8 Km extension through the virtually empty areas of Blackwall,
Leamouth and the Royal Docks to Beckton was required to
stimulate development.   Only a relatively a small part of the
area - at Blackwall and Leamouth has Enterprise Zone
advantages.

26.   The transport approach to the development of the Royals
is fundamentally different from that of the Isle of Dogs in
that the £140 million Royal Docks highway system is being
constructed in advance of the main development, as is the
Beckton Extension of the DLR.   In contrast, in the Isle of
Dogs, the really major highways (including the £300 million
Limehouse Link) only started in 1989, long after development
was well advanced.

27.   This Beckton Extension, work on which stated in 1989, is
being built to a substantially higher standard than the
initial railway and will cost about £250 million.   Part of the
higher cost per Km is caused by inflation, part by the
decision to provide two-car trains on opening day in 1992 and

Fig. 8.   The Isle of Dogs by the year 2000

part by the higher standards (eg concrete beams in place of
steel beams to reduce noise on elevated sections).
Additionally, whilst the great majority of the initial railway
was constructed on existing disused railway, often on viaduct,
in contrast most of the Beckton Extension is on new alignment
and is either on elevated track or in cutting.

28.   Many difficulties had to be overcome before the decision
to go ahead could be given to the Beckton Extension.

29.   Government decided that it was not to be paid for out of
public funds and in the end more than 95% of the cost will be
paid for by the Corporation out of the proceeds of future land
sales.

30.   It was necessary to demonstrate to the satisfaction of
Government that the net cost of the Beckton Extension and its
subsequent (profitable) operation was justified on economic
grounds allowing for the increase in values of both private
and publicly owned land.

31.   It was also necessary for it to pass a far more
stringent test – a test which new road schemes do not have to
pass – it had to be demonstrated that the increase in value of
the land in Corporation ownership was sufficient to fund the

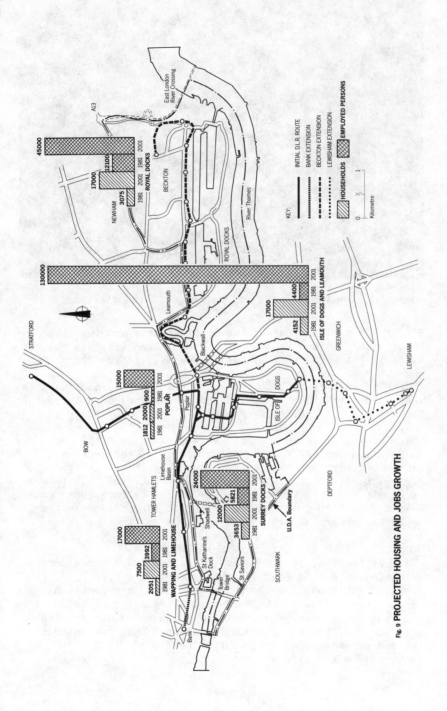

Fig. 9 PROJECTED HOUSING AND JOBS GROWTH

KEY:

INITIAL D.L.R. ROUTE
BANK EXTENSION
BECKTON EXTENSION
LEWISHAM EXTENSION

HOUSEHOLDS

EMPLOYED PERSONS

0   ½   1
Kilometre

Fig. 10.   The Royal Docks before regeneration started

95% of the capital cost of the Beckton Extension that the
Corporation is funding.   No new road schemes will ever be
built if this onerous test were to be applied in future!

32.   It was only because the Corporation's land ownership is
very extensive and anticipated land values are high throughout
the area that the Beckton Extension is now being built.

33.   Provision is made in the agreement between the
Corporation and LRT for the construction of the Beckton
extension, for improvements to be made to the new stations,
during or after construction,   provided that the cost is met
by developers.   To facilitate this special arrangements have
been made in the construction contracts for possible extra
works to be carried out.

DOCKLANDS LIGHT RAILWAY - LEWISHAM EXTENSION
34.   At the time of preparing this paper LRT is considering
promoting an 4.5 Km southern extension to the DLR. If
approved, this would cross under the Thames at Greenwich
through to Lewisham.   It would have the great merit of
reducing the pressure on the initial DLR as passengers from
some parts of the south would be diverted onto the extension
instead of travelling into central London and then out
eastwards to the Isle of Dogs.

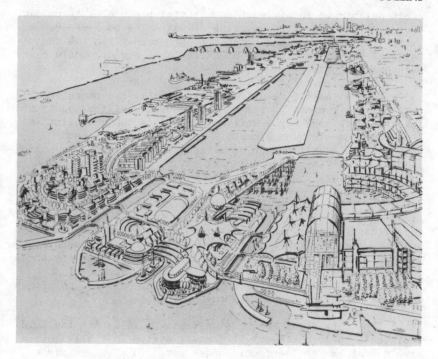

Fig. 11. Part of the Royal Docks in the year 2000

35. It cannot be funded from development gain because very little undeveloped land in public or private ownership would directly benefit although undoubtedly its construction would directly benefit the travelling public as well as developers indirectly.

DOCKLANDS LIGHT RAILWAY - FURTHER EXTENSIONS
36. Government has funded reports into the possible development for housing of derelict land to the east of the Royal Docks.

37. Public transport access to these area would be difficult if it were not for the practicality of extending the Beckton Extension through to serve these new areas. As the areas are heavily polluted, the basic cost of their development would be high and it would probably be touch and go whether the cost of the further extension of the DLR could be funded fully out of enhanced land values.

CONCLUSIONS
38. There can be no doubt that an effective transport system is an essential ingredient of successful regeneration of Inner City areas. This must involve the creation of public transport and, with the inevitable problems of mixing buses and motor vehicles on the same right of way, there will be

great advantages in at least substantial parts of that public
transport being on its own right of way. The cost of such a
system will be heavy and efforts to produce it 'on the cheap'
may well result in problems of reliability and of unduly high
maintenance costs.

39. Because of its relatively high capital and operational
cost a light transit system at the heavy end of the spectrum –
like the Docklands Light Railway – requires dense housing and
commercial development along its route to justify its
construction. Whilst such densities seem achievable in London
it may be that in many provincial cities, systems more akin to
a light tram would be appropriate.

40. The likelihood of being able to recover the capital cost
of a fixed rail system from developers is small, unless the
body financing the transit system is also the predominant land
owner responsible for redevelopment. This would be much less
of a problem if it were possible to raise taxes over the area
that benefits and hypothecate them to the provision of
transport. Other countries do this by, for example, raising a
sales tax – a very buoyant source of income.

41. There are clear financial advantages in making the bold
decision to provide the Light Transit system initially before
development has got seriously under way. This will maximise
the financial return from land sales and ensure that the
development takes full advantage of the enhanced transport
facility. A policy of wait and see what development gets
under way before committing a major rail system may result in
inferior development and problems about funding the railway
out of land receipts. It will rarely be realistic to expect
land holding developers to fund fully a Light Transit system.

42. In the UK it should not be difficult to set aside the
extra Uniform Business Rate resulting from regeneration to pay
for the infrastructure, including the Transit System. However
longstanding Treasury objections in principle make the
likelihood of hypothecation seem rather remote.

4. Light rail transit to stimulate development: the developer's perspective

M. SCHABAS, Transport Manager, Olympia & York

SYNOPSIS. Olympia & York is developing Canary Wharf, a £3 billion project which will form the centrepiece of London's third business district in Docklands. As part of the development agreement, Olympia & York are contributing about £70 million towards upgrading and extension of the Docklands Light Railway. Olympia & York has subsequently agreed to make a major contribution to extention of the Jubilee Underground Line also to Docklands. The paper discusses reasons why Olympia & York was prepared to make these contributions, and also looks at the potential for other private contributions to rail projects in London and around the world.

1. This paper is listed in the programme as presenting 'the developers case for light transit'. For the transport planner and engineer, the idea that a developer would even have a 'case' for light rail may more often be wishful thinking than reality. Speaking first as a transport planner, I know that we have many more rail schemes that we consider 'worthwhile' than we can probably ever convince government to fund. So the idea that developers might also help to make the case for light rail should, I think, be welcome indeed.
2. Before joining Olympia & York I spent two years in Honolulu planning a transit line that makes eminent economic sense, but remains stalled because government will not risk the necessary money in an environment where almost everybody drives a car. Public transport is viewed with suspicion, because its benefits have sometimes been oversold, and operating losses seem to go on forever. Private support will, hopefully, play a critical role in Honolulu because the willingness of developers and investors to put their own money forward will be the best evidence that public investment will also be worthwhile.
3. In London, also, we have seen government hesitate or even simply refuse to invest billions in rail schemes that are strongly supported by planners, and yet with considerably less hesitation approve schemes that are backed by development interests. Politicians see planners as generating schemes with unclear objectives, objectives of sometimes dubious merit, too many unsolved implementation problems, and too long

a payback. Private investor support, even for only a part of the cost of a project, is quite properly seen as evidence that it will have at least some very real benefit to somebody, and therefore probably quite a few benefits to society as a whole.

4. Certainly the Bank Extension to the Docklands Light Railway, which benefits Canary Wharf, also gives enormous benefits to the development of Docklands as a whole. Government was quite content to see the scheme go ahead quickly on the basis of Olympia & York paying half the cost.

5. The case for the Jubilee Extension was somewhat more difficult, mostly because it is a much larger scheme with benefits not just to Canary Wharf and Docklands, but to London as a whole. Our original proposal, to simply build a line from Canary Wharf to Waterloo, suited our needs but did very little for the London Underground network as a whole. London Underground quite properly insisted that we instead contribute to a larger scheme, one which would carry substantial traffic both ways, carrying passengers from East and South London into Westminster and the West End, as well as from the Waterloo to Docklands. The planners thus made sure that London got a better line, but still one that private developers would support financially.

6. Subsequent to the government approving the Jubilee line, we are asked by people involved in other rail schemes around the country if they thought it was realistic for them to get similar private contributions.

7. The circumstances where developers will choose to actively and substantially support rail schemes are fairly rare, certainly very rarely on the scale of Canary Wharf. But then government can only contemplate a few schemes a year, or indeed only one or two at a time even in a city as large as London. So the schemes with private money are likely to take precedence for some years to come. It is certain that governments both here and abroad will look with increasing interest for private support before funding any major scheme. So regardless of one's views on whether private funding is right or wrong, planners are probably wasting their time if they ignore it.

8. Planners must do two things differently if they are to get more private developers actively making and supporting the case for rail transport. First, they must design schemes more specifically attuned to developers' needs. Second, they must do a better job convincing developers that they need to be involved.

9. Developers are businessmen, so they will only support a rail scheme to the extent that it creates value. Creating value is, unfortunately, not as simple as it sometimes seems. Once upon a time it was easy - put up a better building and people will pay to use it. But as our cities have become more complicated, it has become more difficult to create value without also destroying it. Last fall the Public Accounts Committee suggested Docklands developers were reaping windfall profits. A few weeks later, one of the largest went bankrupt,

indicating that they had, on balance, actually created less
value than they destroyed - or spent. Developing is a very
risky business, and the potential rewards reflect the risks.

10. Even assuming a development succeeds, the value which
is created often bears only an indirect relationship to the
usual measures of congestion relief and passenger time savings
that are familiar to transport planners. Developers see value
in rents, which means real money you can put in the bank.
This is quite different from the output of a transportation
forecasting model!

11. To the developer, the value of the time savings may
vary enormously for different types of people, frankly
relating to how important they are, or, in the case of
shoppers, how much they are likely to spend. In the case of
retail traffic, specific details of access time and route may
be extremely important, in ways that are rarely included in
any transport planning process. If light rail planners want
developers to support rail projects, they must tailor their
projects to the needs of developers. I will return to this
with a few examples later.

12. Time is money, and also risk. Developers will hesitate
to get involved in anything that will take a long time to
implement. In the high-risk business of property
development, two years is a long time and a decade might as
well be forever. Yet for a transport planner two years is the
normal length of time for a planning programme, and a decade
is the normal implementation time. If transport planners are
to get developer support, they will need to match the
developer's timeframe.

13. Time and risk also relate to convincing developers to
get involved. Most developers look for opportunities, not
problems. There are always enough problems - getting planning
permission, financing, managing architects and builders,
getting tenants - so the last thing most developers want is to
support a rail line that may not happen.

14. If a developer sees a rail line likely to happen, they
see it as an opportunity and try to to capitalize on it. One
might conclude from the size of this gathering that there are
more light rail planners around than schemes to employ them.
Such is not the case in property development. The most
successful developers can be very choosy, and have learned not
to take the first opportunity that comes along. They are
unlikely to invest time and money in a project that will only
succeed 'if' a proposed light rail scheme moves ahead.

15. Here it is useful to distinguish developers from
property owners. A developer is someone looking to buy land
and invest in it to increase its value. Once a developer
decides to buy the land, they become a property owner with
somewhat different interests. At this point they are
committed to the site, and will certainly support anything
like a new rail line which is likely to add value. But they
are unlikely to make a contribution to costs for two reasons.
First, they probably are already locked into a development

program that will mature long before the rail line is actually built. Although they may achieve higher rents eventually, the fact that the developer was already proceeding indicates that the scheme would be viable even without the rail line.

16. Second, light rail routes are usually planned on the basis of transport need and available routes - most developers will ask why they should pay for something that will be built anyway. Even if the government says the scheme is dependent upon private contributions, there is the obvious problem of the 'free rider'.

EXAMPLES

17. Here are a few examples of how rail schemes do - or do not - attract property developer interest:

London Docklands

18. Here was derelict and mostly vacant land, in an enterprise zone with attractive tax incentives, and only two miles from the City of London and some of the highest property values in the world. Here development was only a matter of when, not if, but the London Docklands Development Corporation could have waited a long time. The light railway provided basic access into an isolated area, although of course many people still drive or travel by bus. More important was that the light railway indicates a public commitment and investment to regeneration - a willingness on the side of government to 'get things done', not just in public transport, but building roads, sewers, and so on.

19. The LDDC was pragmatic and bought the most railway they could with the least money. They were prepared to compromise in order to make the project happen, hoping that if the system was successful in attracting many passengers it could be incrementally upgraded. Actually one month before the initial DLR opened for revenue service, Olympia & York agreed to develop the Canary Wharf project and contribute to the upgrading and extension.

20. My colleague from the LDDC has already shown the Canary Wharf project, which will soon emerge as London's third central business district.

21. The DLR is now being virtually rebuilt from the ground up, to prepare for the projected increased traffic. Despite current complaints about DLR reliability, which should end once the upgrading is completed, one must consider the initial Docklands Light Railway to have been an overwhelming success.

Vancouver

22. One must not let the Docklands experience suggest that all a city need do is build a rail line and wait for the developers to arrive. Docklands is happening because the national and regional economy is basically strong, but this is not always the case. No light railway can overcome a recession!

23.   Vancouver built the Skytrain system just as the local economy - based too heavily on timber and mining - plunged into a deep recession. Some new buildings have now gone up around stations, but much more slowly than in Docklands. Nevertheless, they have had some success in getting property developers to make financial contributions.

24.   At Main Street Station, the transit authority agreed to move the elevated line off the middle of a street and onto a development site. The owner felt this would give better service to his proposed hotel and office complex, and agreed to contribute about $3.00 per square foot once his building was completed. If and when the site is developed, this will probably amount to $3 million - small change in the scale of the project but nothing to ignore. Meanwhile, nothing has yet been built and the contribution is registered on the title to the land.

25.   At another location in Vancouver, BC Transit needed a station but had no clear preference where to put it. They effectively held an auction between three adjacent owners along the line, all of who had outline planning permission to build a regional shopping and office centre. The winner agreed to provide space for a bus interchange, and also make a contribution on the same square foot basis as at Main Street. Of course, while BC Transit got the bus loop right away the developer has very carefully built everything first outside the zone where the contribution is required!

Honolulu

26.   This system has not yet been built, but is at or near the top of the list for new systems in US cities. It is one of the few American schemes which could actually turn an sizeable operating profit. There are also enormous development opportunities, which together probably could pay for the scheme, but here the free rider problem becomes serious. Nobody will offer a contribution for something which will happen sooner or later on its own.

27.   Nevertheless, the route has been planned intentionally to attract as much development potential as possible. The line serves existing centres like Waikiki Beach and the Financial district, but also purposefully runs through major development sites like Kaka'ako, where the state government owns about a hundred acres of prime ocean frontage which it currently uses as a rubbish tip! If the State really wants the rail line, they will probably figure out a way to recover some of the cost by developing this land.

28.   Elsewhere, stations have been designed to link directly into existing and planned shopping centres. Provided developers make appropriate contributions, the stations can be designed with 'stacked platforms' to route passengers through the shopping between trains and buses. Again, a developer will weigh any contribution against the extra revenue that will be generated - if rail passengers are mostly budget

tourists or school children, they won't spend much money anyway.

Jubilee Extension

29. As most of you probably know, Olympia & York is now involved in a second rail line to Docklands. This arose originally in response to an invitation from Paul Channon, then Secretary of State for Transport, for private transport schemes. We suggested a new tube line across London, and offered to fund an initial section from Waterloo Station to Canary Wharf. We actually completed preliminary engineering and parliamentary plans in November 1988, but London Underground deferred the deposit of the bill, mostly because it was not part of their overall development plan. After some delay, the East London Rail Study recommended an extension of the Jubilee line from Green Park on much the same route, and they are currently promoting a private bill for this.

30. As a property developer, our interest in the Jubilee extension has been predicated on the same points I have already mentioned.

31. Our first concern was that the line be built quickly. Consequently, we proposed that it follow a 'clean' route mostly under or along existing rail corridors. This minimizes the potential noise and property impacts.

32. We have also proposed a pro-active approach to consultation with community groups, local governments, English heritage, and so on. We know as a property developer that it is in one's best interest to work with these groups and not to fight them. In the nineteenth century railway's might be able to ignore local residents, but not today. Moreover, community groups know their community best and can actually often help. They often have better ideas than the technical experts we pay for advice!

33. Similarly, London Underground prepared a comprehensive environmental statement even though this is not strictly required by Law.

34. Second, we saw it as important that the line serve Waterloo station, a major commuter and Channel Tunnel terminal. Long before anyone dreamed of Docklands becoming a business centre, a Jubilee extension had been planned that missed Waterloo and went instead via Charing Cross. London Underground recognized the changing role of the line, and this was supported not just by other Docklands developers, but also by the transport modelling which actually showed more traffic on the line following the Waterloo route.

35. Third, we have suggested that the line be conceived as a high speed regional service, possibly with new, faster, and more comfortable trains. It is more than a quarter century since London Underground built a new line, and the rest of the world has made a few advances since then. We have also argued against simply building a station every half mile, and have suggested thorough economic and financial analysis of system

elements as each deep tube station can easily cost £30 million.

36. Last, but certainly not least, we agreed with London Underground that it was essential that the new line is not just good for Canary Wharf, but for London. Otherwise one could never expect it to win much public support. While the wider benefits of the Jubilee extension have not received wide press coverage, it will provide significant relief to London tube congestion. The East London Rail Study showed that the line actually diverts more traffic off the congested Central and District lines bound for Westminster, than from Waterloo to Canary Wharf. It also relieves lines that feed the DLR at Bank, including parts of the Northern line, the Circle line, and even the Victoria line.

37. By actually diverting some new office growth out of the congested City and West End, Docklands will provide long term relief in a way that no new line through the centre can match. The Jubilee Extension is essentially a bypass, taking traffic and development around the City and out to the vast land resources in Docklands.

38. We look forward to its rapid passage through parliament and speedy construction!

THE FUTURE

39. The DLR Bank Extension and Jubilee Extension are certainly not the end of the story of private funding of rail lines in the regeneration of East London. Already, developers of Bishopsgate are reported to have made an offer to fund part of the cost to extend the East London Line. Similarly, the London Borough of Lewisham is apparently finding some developer interest in extending the Docklands Light Railway to their patch.

40. Of even more immediate significance is the decision of British Urban Development, a consortium of eleven major companies, to pay additional costs to divert the Jubilee Line very slightly to serve the Greenwich Peninsula. Here the developer's contribution is not only useful to reduce the cost to the taxpayer, it is also insurance that BUD will actually develop the site so there will be passengers on the trains.

41. Canary Wharf is Olympia and York's first development in the United Kingdom. We are extremely pleased with the spirit of co-operation which has developed between ourselves, the Departments of the Environment and Transport, the LDDC, the local Boroughs, London Regional Transport, London Underground, London Buses and the DLR. The transport infrastructure being put in place will be second to none and wholly complementary to the emergence of London's new third business centre.

Discussion on papers 1–4

R. A. NEWPORT, <u>Chief Engineer (Public Transport), Avon County Council</u>

First let me make clear that all the local authorities in the area - Avon County Council, Bristol City Council and the other District Councils - have welcomed the concept of an LRT system as a valuable potential contribution to the transport system in the county. But the origin of the scheme, from a private promoter, is unprecedented in recent times and has therefore presented the authorities with an unusual challenge.

Avon County Council has from the beginning sought to co-operate with the initiative - though not without doubts about particular aspects, many of which remain to be definitely resolved. It has become apparent that the system will only be constructed if it can attract substantial sums of public money, through a Section 56 grant from both the Government and the County Council.

Because of this realization, and its wish to see all the aspects fully examined, the County Council has recently resolved to take its involvement with the project a stage further. It is now exploring with the promoter the possibility of entering into a joint venture agreement. Such an agreement would seek to formalize the co-operative arrangements already in existence. Although it would not in the final analysis inhibit the rights and responsibilities of either the promoter or the local authorities, it is hoped that the agreement will provide, in particular, a satisfactory process for incorporation of the political dimension which, as Mr Taplin notes in Paper 1, is a crucial factor in any transport issue.

Finally, let me make it clear to any public authorities that believe that the promotion of a scheme by an outside body is an easy way forward, it is not. Whatever the origins of the proposal satisfactory progress will only be achieved by a full recognition of the impact on the resources of the local authorities, and by recognition on the other side that their contribution is vital.

C. F. BONNETT, <u>formerly Docklands Light Railway, now London Transport International</u>

The session question `Do you need it?', in my opinion should be extended at the planning stage to include `and if so what do you need?'. This relates not so much to the type of system but to the <u>extent</u> of what is needed. In most cases financial support is extremely limited so the vital question relates to the thinness and thickness of the spreading of the butter. Without doubt there is great danger in spreading it too thin, especially when systems are overtaken by their own success and upgrading and extension is required.

As managing director, I was responsible for bringing into operation the Docklands Light Railway and for operating the railway for the first 18 months. Without doubt the railway acted as a catalyst for development in Docklands but the thinness of the spread of the butter in the initial railway has caused very severe problems and undue restrictions in operation whilst upgrading is being carried out. It is tragic that the new light railway which is such a draw to overseas visitors and Londoners alike, is at the moment having to be closed down in the evenings and at the weekend. A good analogy is trying to rebuild the inadequate hub of a rotating wheel to carry extra load at faster speeds without stopping the wheel!

I would recommend to all those now embarking on the planning of light rail systems to ensure that the <u>initial sector</u> of the system fulfils the following criteria

(1)   all structures must from the outset be strong enough for the maximum likely frequency and length of trains when the system is in its final finished state

(2)   the signalling system on the initial sector must be able to cope with the likely final frequency and length without modification

(3)   there must be a constant guard against over-sophistication of the system.

Adhering to these principles may mean a small reduction in the extent of the initial sector but this, in my opinion, will be well worth while in the long term.

D. GUTTERIDGE, Charles Haswell & Partners

My firm has led a study team for Swire Properties Ltd for a possible railway connecting southern districts to central on Hong Kong island. There is considerable private interest in funding such a railway, the cost of the project being recovered through property development. The Government had identified a need for such a railway to alleviate road congestion but it is relatively low on their list of priorities. The three development companies interested have all employed consultants to study the routes and prepare reasonably accurate cost estimates. The latter is very important to the possible providers of funds as they need to know the expected return on their capital outlay. Proposals for funding and construction of the railway are now with the Government.

DR L. LESLEY, Liverpool Polytechnic

There is a danger that light rail is `flavour of the month' - too many systems are chasing too little money, and this means that some good schemes will fail (e.g. the problems in Sheffield). Nearly 20 years ago Cabtrack was to be the transport system of the future!

Are we prepared to give public transport priority? Over 10 years ago Nottingham launched its `Zone and Collar' scheme, where buses would get green phases at traffic signals, while private cars were delayed. The political uproar saw Zone and Collar abandoned within three months.

In Zurich 90% of the public transport system is segregated with `waiting time zero' at traffic signals. Will the Department of Transport issue guide notes for traffic signals favouring public transport?

To give public transport priority means we have to use our cars less. Are we prepared to do this?
The London Docklands experience of generating large planning gains, and developer profits enough to pay for light rail, may not be achievable in the poorer provinces, where much greater levels of public finance and support will be necessary.

B. COLLINS, Paper 3

I was the Chief Officer in Nottingham and Nottinghamshire during the early to mid 1970s, responsible for the introduction and the abandonment of the Zone and Collar experiment. It lasted very much longer than three months. It was abandoned quite simply because it proved impossible to delay private cars sufficiently to induce motorists to transfer to buses, not because of political uproar. My experience then and since, has convinced me that the only way

DISCUSSION

of creating space on congested highways for public transport
and goods vehicles, is by the introduction of wide scale
sophisticated road pricing.

E. LAWRENCE, Eurocap-Transportech
   I wish to lend support to the Paper by Mr Joos. I travel on
the Zurich LRV system regularly, as it provides a punctual
service which enables me to plan business meetings in the city
with complete confidence. Only once in twelve years have I
experienced major problems, and that occasion was when one of
the worst blizzards ever struck Zurich overnight.
   The Zurich LRV system is part of an overall public transport
system which includes buses, trolleybuses, funicular railways,
the main line railway, the new 'S' bahn, the Postbus service
and even the lake steamers. Connections between each of the
above are carefully planned and give an exceptional service
right across the city and into the surrounding towns and
villages. It really is a model which we in the UK should
study carefully.

J. GLOVER, Colin Buchanan & Partners
   I think we must decide what we are trying to achieve. Is it
positive discrimination in favour of public transport as in
Zurich, to allow the maximum possible use of private cars, or
to contrive a 'middle of the road' approach?
Light rapid transit was a solution looking for a problem. It
now represents a solution which, in part anyway, may match the
problem of traffic congestion in cities. The concept of LRT
and what it can do needs to be sold to a wider audience - the
Government and its agencies, and the general public. LRT
cannot be introduced painlessly - rights of way are needed,
and it will cost money. But it can still be an excellent
community investment.

J. EDWARDS, Halcrow Fox & Associates
   In order to optimize the use of any light rail system
adequate car parking facilities must be provided at central
city locations. Only in this way will car owners - as a
rapidly increasing number of people are - be attracted to
light rail transit.

I. HARRIS, <u>Greater Manchester Passenger Transport Executive</u>
My contribution concerns the need for studies. There are
three principal potential sources of funding for LRT schemes:
developers, private sector operators, and the public sector
(mainly through the Section 56 grant). In the case of
developers, it needs to be understood that Canary Wharf was a
very special case. An enormous development surrounded by
water with very poor highway access. Developers elsewhere,
especially in provincial cities, will see roads and parking as
much more relevant to their needs than light rail. A lot of
work is necessary to convince them of the value of LRT.

It has been suggested that private sector builders and
operators would require fewer studies. Greater Manchester
PTE's experience is precisely the opposite. Each of the three
bidding consortia for Metrolink was given full access to the
extensive patronage and revenue forecasts undertaken for the
PTE, yet each commissioned various types of survey and
forecast from their own consultants.

Most importantly, we have the Section 56 grant. When the
new rules first began to emerge from the Department of
Transport, the PTE group told the Department that the new
rules with their great emphasis on non-user benefit,
especially the relief of congestion, would stretch existing
forecasting methodology to the limits and substantially
increase the cost and duration of studies. This has indeed
proved to be the case. For instance to meet the Department of
Transport's requirements, Greater Manchester PTE is currently
spending over £400 000 on studies to justify the conversion of
the Manchester-Oldham-Rochdale railway to LRT - a line which
most planners and engineers in the area would consider to be
an 'obvious' case for conversion.

D. S. HELLEWELL, <u>Greater Manchester Metrolink</u>
For a rail-based mode of transport, light rail is a very
flexible system in terms of the markets it can serve, the
capacity of service it can provide and the choice of
alignments and locations. To be cost-effective it is
necessary to select the right blend of features. The first
step is, therefore, to identify the problem that is to be
solved, and define the objectives. Then look at the modes of
transport that are available to meet these. Light rail may
well be among those modes to be considered but it is not a
panacea to all transport problems.

Light rail's capacity range is between 5000 and 15 000
passengers per hour i.e. between the upper ranges possible
with buses and the lower range with 'heavy' rail. Individual
circumstances may make it cost-effective at demand figures
above or below those quoted. The essential feature of light
rail is its flexibility. However, this places the onus on the

promoter of a light rail scheme to select the most cost-
effective mode and, if it is light rail, to embody those
features most suitable.

R. A. MCKITTRICK, Partner, Scott Wilson Kirkpatrick
The Nottingham LRT study is still at a feasibility stage but
already most of the elements referred to in these papers have
been covered in the study for which I am Scott Wilson
Kirkpatrick's Project Director.
We initially identified nineteen potential routes and
reduced these to six by comparing each one with a long list of
criteria, including the following.

(1)   The use of abandoned railway reserves where relevant.
(2)   Penetration of Nottingham's Task Force Area to provide
      regeneration and methods of providing transport for
      unemployed people seeking work.
(3)   The potential for accessing sites with major development
      potential.
(4)   The possibility of reducing congestion on existing main
      roads.
(5)   Comparing the LRT system with existing transport modes
      and acceptance of the fact that in some areas these may
      be perfectly acceptable.
(6)   Having continuous discussions with potential private
      sector operators as well as potential developers.
(7)   Considering the introduction of major park and ride
      facilities.
(8)   Considering relief of inner city congestion by
      reorganizing existing traffic patterns.
(9)   Taking positive moves to connect the Midland Railway
      Station with the existing commercial and shopping areas.
(10) Considering the implications of the reopening of the
      Mansfield to Nottingham railway line.

All of these have been, and are being, considered and will
feed into the Section 56 grant application as at present that
is necessary to satisfy the Department of Transport.

5. Evaluating alternative proposals

W. J. TYSON, MA (Econ), Consultant Economist

SYNOPSIS. Although LRT is cheaper than conventional railways to construct and to operate, it is a substantial investment which needs to be systematically evaluated. Until recently evaluation would have used conventional economic criteria and social cost-benefit analysis following the principles used for road schemes. However, policy developments since 1986 have changed this. They include:

- bus deregulation
- revised Section 56 grant criteria
- private sector finance.

Section 1 of the paper traces the evaluation of these developments and their implications for evaluation.
Section 2 discusses the evaluation methods to be used and in particular examines the issue of evaluation of external benefits which form the heart of the new grant criteria.
Section 3 discusses briefly wider issues of evaluation methodology.

1. THE POLICY CONTEXT

1. Evaluation is an aid to decision making and any evaluation technique needs to reflect criteria used by decision-makers who, until the mid 1980s, were central and local government. The criteria they used was the economic efficiency of the transport system and, ultimately, the economy as a whole. Social cost-benefit analysis was extensively applied to investments in roads and urban public transport.

2. Evaluations would quantify costs (capital and operating) and benefits to users and non-users in the transport sector regardless of whether they were reflected in revenues. This was the only practical method of evaluation as no market existed for urban public transport and conventional financial evaluation would have been impossible to apply.

3. During the 1980s three policy developments radically changed the situation:

(a)   bus deregulation, under the 1985 Transport Act, created
      a free market for some urban public transport. The Act
      broke the financial link between bus and rail services;

(b)   private capital was seen as a possible source of funding
      for light rail schemes;

(c)   the government proposed, in 1989, to change the criteria
      on which it decides the amount of grant it will give
      towards the cost of public transport infrastructure
      investments under Section 56 of the 1968 Transport Act.

4. This latter change is fundamental. When Section 56
grants were given in the past, the criterion was that net
benefits of a scheme should exceed capital cost. Grant was
based on the capital cost and given at various rates – most
commonly 50%. Under the new criteria grant becomes a 'last
resort' source of funding and is used specifically to pay for
external benefits which cannot be captured in revenues. The
most important benefit is relief of traffic congestion which
accrues to road users staying in the roads and cannot be
captured from them by the LRT operator. Some benefits, for
example, to those using LRT no longer enter into the criteria
for grant.

5. The system of financing may be summarised as:

(a)   promoters need to maximise the amount they raise from
      users of the system in fares and use this to defray
      part of the capital cost;

(b)   benefits to developers should, where possible, be
      captured to help finance the scheme;

(c)   if (a) and (b) are insufficient government will
      consider Section 56 grant if it can be justified by
      external benefits.

6. The implications for evaluation are:

(1)   post bus deregulation there is increasing emphasis on
      the financial performance of a light rail investment.
      In particular, before deregulation, revenue from
      passengers transferring from bus to LRT would not
      have counted in the evaluation as they were a transfer
      between one part of the public purse (bus subsidies)
      and another (LRT). However, since deregulation
      revenue gained from buses counts in full. It is
      important, therefore, to evaluate all aspects of the
      revenue gained from modal switching;

(2)   if the private sector is going to risk its money it
      will want to see a more detailed evaluation of the
      costs and the revenues than was the case when the
      public sector alone was involved;

(3)   the new grant criteria places more emphasis on
      measuring external benefits and maximising revenue.

7. In summary there is much more emphasis on the financial effects of LRT investments as well as their wider economic and transportation network implications.

2. EVALUATION REQUIREMENTS

8. There can be several parties involved in financing an LRT scheme and each will want an evaluation of its effects on what it considers to be appropriate criteria. They are:

(a) central government – criterion: non-user benefits;
(b) local government – criterion: local transport impact and economic regeneration
(c) private sector – criterion: costs and revenues.

Three types of evaluation are needed:

(a) an economic evaluation of the project as a whole;
(b) a specific evaluation of non-user benefits;
(c) a financial appraisal of revenues and costs.

9. <u>Economic Evaluation</u>. The economic evaluation needs to take into account all costs and benefits of the investment. It therefore must include:

- capital costs
- operating costs
- benefits to users of the system
- benefits and disbenefits to users of other modes
- impact on traffic congestion
- impact on costs of operating other modes (eg bus, heavy rail)
- accident costs
- environmental benefits and costs.

This type of economic evaluation has been applied to urban public transport and road investments for many years. For example, Tyne & Wear Metro was justified on this basis.

10. The importance of this evaluation is:

(a) it shows the total benefits of the investment in transport and economic terms;
(b) by quantifying user benefits it provides input to the financial appraisal which will be looking at ways of capturing these benefits in revenue;
(c) it provides the estimates of non-user benefits needed for the Section 56 grant evaluation;
(d) it can also provide a framework for determining whether any contributions from third parties e.g. developers, are feasible;
(e) by including all the costs and benefits it is a means of ensuring consistency with the other evaluations – in effect – it is a "blue-print" for the other evaluations.

11. Section 56 Grant. Non-user benefits form the basis of the government's decision on Section 56 grant. The rationale is that non-users who benefit cannot be made to contribute and if the benefits are to be taken into account the public purse must pay. The benefits are:

(a) relief of traffic congestion. Light rail schemes will have an impact on congestion if they attract car and bus users. Traffic flows will decrease and remaining vehicles will travel faster giving rise to the benefits. There may also be adverse effects on congestion if street running reduces capacity for other road users. Both have to be taken into account;

(b) reduction in accidents. Rail based modes have fewer accidents per passenger mile than road vehicles. Thus a road to light rail switch should reduce accidents and to the extent that there are external elements of benefits (eg reduced NHS and police costs) they can be included in the evaluation. Again, any adverse impacts need to be included;

(c) environmental benefits. These are again assuming importance in evaluations and, in general, public transport is far less damaging to the environment than the car. There are therefore benefits in terms of reduced noise, atmosphere pollution etc;

(d) economic regeneration. If a light rail scheme can act as a catalyst in the economic regeneration of an area there are wider benefits to the economy as a whole which the government is prepared to consider in its grant decision.

12. Financial Evaluation. This concentrates on:-

- operating costs
- revenues

and the contributions which any surplus of revenue over cost can, over the life of the project, make to the capital cost of the scheme.

13. However, it needs to go further and examine the funding of the whole scheme to demonstrate that it will be possible from all available sources to assemble the funds needed to build it.

Quantifying Benefits and Costs

14. Non-User Benefits. There is insufficient time to deal in detail with all the issues. The main area of concern is external benefits and some of the problems which arise are:-

(a)   models to estimate traffic congestion benefits are often
      too coarse (eg conurbation transport models), or too
      complex (eg congested assignment models). More work is
      needed to develop a suitable model to estimate
      congestion impacts;

(b)   estimating the switch between modes if a light rail
      scheme is introduced is extremely important.
      Increasing use is being made of models based on stated
      preference techniques and further development of this
      work is likely;

(c)   determining the proportion of accident benefits which
      are external (ie not enjoyed by the person switching
      from road to rail) is a complex area in which unresolved
      issues remain;

(d)   environmental benefits present problems. A lot of work
      on quantifying the effects of different forms of
      transport on the environment has been carried out.
      Much less is known about values to be placed on these
      benefits although development of stated preference
      research should provide a means of overcoming this gap
      in the knowledge;

(e)   economic development benefits are particularly
      difficult to deal with because the impact of a light
      rail scheme needs to be disentangled from all other
      factors contributing to regeneration. Further work is
      most certainly needed here.

15.   Much more work needs to be done. In the conurbations
the PTE Group have recognised this and have commissioned
Halcrow Fox and Associates to carry out some of this research.
They should report in 1990. Other research will be carried
out as part of the evaluation of projects currently being
developed.

16.   User Benefits. Most user benefits comprise time
savings. In economic evaluation it has been usual to value
these at a uniform rate per person but making distinctions
between in-work and non-work time and between in-vehicle and
walking and waiting time. This overlooks the fact that people
all have their own values of time. It begins to matter when
the question of converting time savings into revenue is raised.
Finding a fare structure which maximises the amount of benefit
converted into revenue is a major challenge for any promoter
or operator of a scheme.

17.   Summary. The relationships between the three
evaluations can be seen in the table below which shows how the
elements in the economic evaluation appear in the others. A
cross (x) means that they appear in the same form. If they
are in a different form this is indicated.

	Economic	S56	Financial
Capital costs	X		X
Operating costs	X		X
Effect on other modes	X		Possible Contribution?
User benefits	X		Revenue
Benefits to users of other modes	X		
Non-user benefits	X	X	Section 56 grant
Development benefits			Possible Contributions?
Economic regeneration	X	X	Section 56 grant

3. WIDER ISSUES OF EVALUATION METHODOLOGY

18. There are several other factors which have to be taken into account in evaluating a light rail proposal and a number of issues are raised by the current approach to evaluation.

19. Options. It is important to consider a wide range of options in evaluating a light-rail proposal. In particular, where it is replacing or enhancing an existing railway (eg in Manchester) options would include closing altogether and retaining the heavy rail service. This can be beneficial to the justification because it may indicate that a proportion of the capital cost will need to be spent on the other options. This will reduce the net cost of the scheme. In the case of an entirely new scheme the option of not building it may involve high spending on roads and this needs to be taken into the evaluation.

20. Competition. Urban public transport is now a competitive market. Any light rail scheme will have to win its customers from other modes. For evaluations, this implies that the justification must be sufficiently robust to withstand competition from buses and cars. This is usually dealt with by sensitivity testing as no one knows what bus operators will do. However, it is often possible to judge whether a particular competitive strategy can be sustained in the long-term or not. Experience with Manchester Metrolink indicates that light rail can compete effectively and that bus operators have more to gain by feeding passengers than by direct competition.

21. Consistency. The biggest issue in many people's minds when the new Section 56 grant criteria were announced was that urban public transport was being treated differently from roads. The Section 56 criterion is not the same as the criterion used to evaluate and finance road schemes. By insisting that user benefits are captured in revenues the criteria will mean that not all user benefits are counted as they would be for a road scheme.

22. The critical factor in ensuring comparability is the "passmark". If both road and light rail schemes were required to obtain the same ratio of benefit to cost to be acceptable there would be bias towards the road schemes. In effect a lower rate of benefits per pound of cost needs to be applied

to light rail than to roads to make up for the fact that not all benefits from light rail schemes can be counted. This complex area is one which has yet to be resolved and will be debated for some time to come.

4. CONCLUSIONS
23. The main conclusions from this brief survey of evaluation methods are:

(1) it is necessary to carry out more than one evaluation of a scheme;

(2) the evaluations must be consistent;

(3) further development of evaluation methods is needed;

(4) the question of consistency between different evaluation criteria needs to be resolved;

(5) non-user benefits are important for grant applications;

(6) user-benefits need to be turned into revenue.

6. Ridership prediction and revenue estimation

A. LAST, Director, The MVA Consultancy

SYNOPSIS   Appropriate, sensitive demand and revenue forecasts are essential for the successful planning of Light Transit Systems. The paper reviews the requirements for forecasting methods, outlines some of the techniques that are available, and illustrates the application of the methods to specific schemes.

INTRODUCTION

1.   The fundamental rationale of a potential LRT scheme is that it should carry passengers. Forecasting how many passengers will be carried, and the consequences in operational, financial and economic terms is therefore central to LRT planning.

2.   There are a number of reasons for the current surge of interest in innovative public transport schemes within the UK.   However, the practical difficulties of implementing a major scheme are severe.   Many of these difficulties stem from the need to address a wide constituency of interested parties. Most will have their own perspective on what is required of patronage and revenue forecasts.

3.   Consequently, the demands placed upon the skill of the forecasters, and the techniques available to them, have never been greater. This paper identifies some of the methods that are currently being used in practical studies, and shows how they have been used to influence the design and evolution of schemes.

4.   In the next section, we discuss the variety of requirements for demand forecasts that may need to be addressed in nurturing a scheme from first inception to implementation. We then go on to list some of the techniques that can be used to satisfy these requirements. Finally, we will describe how these methods have been applied in helping progress a number of schemes towards implementation.

THE REQUIREMENTS

5.   Just as there is no universally correct technological solution to transport problems, so there is no standard methodology for deriving demand forecasts that is appropriate in all circumstances. In fact, requirements vary widely, depending crucially upon who will be the "consumer" of the resulting predictions.

6.   Also, demand forecasts are inherently uncertain. Even with vast resources, the ultimate accuracy of forecasts in certain circumstances will always be in doubt. However, in general, the more money devoted to research, then the more the confidence in the results. Thus the users of forecasts need to be aware that absolute accuracy is unlikely, but that - to some extent - accuracy can be improved at a price. Moreover, not only money may need to be expended to increase reliability, but also elapsed time - which may be a crucial element where a scheme must exploit a narrow window of opportunity. Thus it is important to establish what decisions flow from a particular forecasting output, and in particular, choose an approach that is appropriate for the stage of evolution of the scheme.

The Evolution of a Scheme

7.   We tend to be most aware of the LRT schemes that are nearing implementation stage. In some cases, they have emerged from a lengthy gestation period stretching back decades. However, many of the tentative schemes now under study are relatively new, at least in their present incarnation. In idealised terms, there is therefore an evolutionary process, in which ideas for a scheme are gradually given more

substance, as studies take place which replace
initial assumptions and "guesstimates" with
soundly based research.

8.   Within this process, demand forecasts
and revenue estimates will play an important part
in shaping the scheme, both in technical terms
(eg alignment, service characteristics,
technology) and also in optimising its
worthwhileness and feasibility.

9.   Ultimately, demand forecasts will
generate the measures of economic and financial
performance that will largely determine whether
or not the scheme is implemented. For the
final "go" or "no-go" decisions, the forecasts
clearly need to be as reliable as possible.
However, decisions at preceding stages, in which
the sums at risk are much smaller, do not require
such reliability. It is clearly inappropriate to
spend £100,000 on demand forecasts in order to
determine whether or not to spend £10,000 on very
preliminary studies of other aspects.

10.   Consequently, forecasting techniques
should be appropriate to circumstances. The
critical question is whether forecasts will be
sufficiently reliable for the immediate
decisions. That of course depends upon the
decision makers, and their particular interests.

The Interested Parties

11.   Who are the consumers of demand
forecasts? And what are their questions?

12.   Interested parties will include:

  • the public at large;
  • all affected local authorities;
  • central government, and the Department
    of Transport in particular;
  • developers and land owners;
  • the business community, in the broad
    sense of retailers, office tenants,
    etc.;
  • bankers;
  • other private sector interests,
    especially potential participants in
    the design, construction or operation
    of the scheme.

Clearly, the promoter of the scheme will also have its own interests, as well as the need to satisfy other parties who can facilitate - or obstruct -the implementation of the scheme.

13.   The questions that demand forecasts could provide answers to include:

- how many passengers?
- what revenue will be generated from passenger fares?
- how many car users will be attracted off the road?
- how many bus passengers will the bus operators lose?
- what is the peak load at the peak loading point?

14.   However, it is the consequences of these answers rather than the "raw" results, that are relevant to most of the interests. In particular, the forecasts will generate the major input into many of the measures of economic and financial performance that will critically determine feasibility.

Sensitivity to What?

15.   Demand forecasts are not simply an end product, but should be part of the overall process of "designing" the scheme, in the broadest sense. Most obviously, forecasts should inform technical design issues - such as the capacity that should be provided - but they also have a role in refining "softer" aspects of the scheme, such as the overall funding strategy. The best example of this is in the use of demand models to refine fare revenue assumptions, by testing of a range of alternative fare levels and systems.

16.   Clearly, to be effective, the modelling processes must be sensitive to those aspects of the scheme that can be adjusted. Any good public transport demand model should be sensitive to the basic characteristics of service level, alignment, speed, etc., but additional aspects may need to be included to satisfy all parties.

17.   In particular, as the impact of a system on highway congestion acquires a high profile, forecasting methods will increasingly

have to make provision for much more detailed
modelling of the interactions between the public
transport network and the highway system. The
Government's draft guidelines for applications
for Section 56 (of the 1968 Transport Act) Grant
place great emphasis on the need to justify
capital subsidy by demonstrating benefits from
congestion relief. Consequently, demand
forecasts may now have to concentrate as much on
the proportion of users switching from road as on
existing public transport passengers.

THE TECHNIQUES

18. Demand forecasts can be derived from
many different sources. The techniques
discussed here are primarily those that have
found immediate application in the development of
specific LRT schemes.

The Role of Data Collection

19. Demand forecasts cannot be conjured out
of thin air, and to be credible must have some
tangible basis in observed local travel patterns.
However, the extent to which observable
passengers today will constitute a significant
proportion of the passengers of tomorrow's rapid
transit system will depend upon the nature and
ambitions of the individual scheme.

20. As the changes brought about by a
scheme become further removed from observable
"reality", then models must be brought more and
more into play. Bus deregulation has
significantly reduced the ability of planning
authorities to collect reliable data on existing
public transport passengers. As a result, in
some cases models have to be used more
extensively than would otherwise have been
necessary to hypothesise the effects of the
scheme.

21. However, major surveys of existing
travel patterns may not be relevant - or
appropriate. During the early stages of scheme
development, it may be sufficient to use broad
indicators of potential patronage, perhaps
derived from sources such as the Census, to help
inform the critical decisions. Crude "back of
the envelope" calculations do have their place,
but at the level of determining whether

substantial expenditure in researching a scheme is worthwhile, rather than in attempting sophisticated evaluations.

22.   With the furthest advanced schemes, ideal data sources have rarely been available, and could not be generated within acceptable time or money constraints. Consequently, modelling strategies have had to be derived that are oriented towards satisfying the requirements of demand forecasts by making the greatest possible use of existing data and modelling resources. With the schemes that are at an earlier stage, there is more scope for fresh data collection. However, it is still essential to devise an overall data and modelling strategy that will deliver the necessary results at the right time and to the necessary levels of accuracy.

The Scope of Demand Models

23.   An LRT scheme is likely to change passenger travel habits in a number of ways:

- existing public transport passengers will change the way they travel through the public transport network (reassignment);
- users of cars will divert to the public transport system (modal choice);
- some travellers will change the origins and/or destinations of their journeys (redistribution);
- some new trips will be made that were not made before (generation).

24.   Although this analysis of change is in theory well recognised in the structure of the conventional transport planning model, in practice, confidence in the ability of planners to predict these changes rapidly decreases as one goes down this list. Patronage forecasts based on assumptions about reassignment of existing passengers should be relatively reliable; modal choice assumptions less so; and redistribution and generation effects are highly uncertain.

25.   Consequently, in seeking "bankable" forecasts, it behoves the promoter to maximise the share of patronage generated from existing public transport use, and to a lesser extent

modal transfer, because other elements will be increasingly discounted because of their inherent uncertainties.

Modelling the Public Transport Network

26.   Given the importance of accurately portraying the attractiveness of the typical LRT scheme relative to existing public transport modes, good modelling of the public transport network is likely to be essential. In particular, the potential for patronage loss or gain arising from the actions of independent bus operators will almost inevitably have to be explored in depth at some stage in the scheme's development.

27.   This implies the need for an operational bus network model, capable of reflecting the impacts of different bus routeing, service level and fares strategies not only on the LRT, but also on the bus operators themselves.

28.   The modelling of competition between LRT and bus, or between LRT and heavy rail, need not necessarily be carried out through the assignment process. Explicit sub-mode choice modelling has performed a useful role in identifying the market to be addressed by the LRT, and also by facilitating testing of general assumptions about competitive responses.

Modal Choice Models

29.   Most formal demand modelling tends to be directed towards modal choice decisions, because it is the obvious focus of policy debate, and also is reasonably well researched.

30.   Conventional mode choice models attempt to predict the proportions of travellers choosing to make specific geographical journeys by each of the available modes, most obviously, by public transport and private transport. The proportion is a function of the estimated travel times and costs of each mode, together with some parameters that determine the sensitivity of the choice to the differences in times and cost.

31.   Because LRT is so new to the UK, there is minimal practical experience to help determine the parameters appropriate to LRT choice. Consequently, assumptions must be made about how the inherent characteristics of LRT compare with, say, other public transport modes, such as urban buses or "heavy" rail services. Thus an important part of the data collection and modelling strategy should allow appropriate cross-elasticities, and modal biasses, to be calibrated to the specific situation.

32.   However, there is scope for establishing a statistical basis for judging how passengers relate individual journey characteristics, such as travelling and waiting time, or quality of ride and higher probabilities of standing. These trade-offs can be measured by "Stated Preference" techniques, which can usefully contribute to, but provide only part of the analysis required to set up a modal choice model.

Stated Preference Techniques

33.   This set of techniques encompass special types of surveys and analysis designed to identify how respondents would trade-off different attributes. There are a variety of ways in which the principles are applied, but typically, respondents are specially selected to be representative of the types of traveller of interest. The respondent is asked to rank a series of hypothetical situations (all of which have been selected to be credible, within the frame of experience of the respondent), and which have been chosen to reveal the relative weightings placed upon the attributes.

34.   Attributes might include:

- waiting time;
- in-vehicle time;
- fare paid, or out-of-pocket cost;
- ride quality;
- aspects of the interior design of the vehicle;
- station facilities etc.

35.   Consequently, a picture can be built up of the most important features that potential users would seek in a new mode, such as LRT.

However, this insight would not in itself allow
aggregate predictions to be made of the number of
passengers that would actually be attracted on a
particular corridor.

Other Modelling Methods

36.   While the techniques described above
have a particular relevance to LRT scheme demand
forecasting, most other transport planning tools
can have their place in a study. Almost
inevitably, forecasts will need to be made of a
future situation in which there are changes to
land use and development patterns; conventional
trip generation and trip distribution methods may
need to be applied in order to reflect the
changes brought about in passenger travel
patterns.

37.   Because of the current requirements for
justification of Section 56 Grant, an increasing
emphasis is also having to be given to highway
modelling, of which there are a number of
distinct aspects which need to be considered:

- public/private modal choice models will
  generally need to be driven by inputs
  of estimated travel times and costs by
  car

- the effect of predicted diversions of
  car users on the level of service
  offered by the highway network may need
  to be evaluated, requiring detailed
  modelling of the highway network;

- where street running of LRT is
  envisaged, there will be major changes
  to the capacity characteristics of the
  highway links along which LRT will run,
  which will need to be reflected in the
  above.

38.   It is clear therefore that the
requirements of LRT patronage forecasting and
revenue estimation may demand a very wide range
of skills and techniques, working at a variety of
levels of sophistication from the crude to the
highly refined.

THE APPLICATIONS

39.   LRT schemes vary enormously in scope
and timing. What constitutes a "typical" scheme
can no doubt give rise to considerable debate.
Some individual examples can however illustrate
how the ideas described above can be put into
practice.

Initial Studies

40.   At an early stage in the evolution of a
scheme, there are likely to be considerable
doubts as to whether there are any interesting
possibilities worth exploring. Consequently, it
is important to establish broad, low cost
indicators of the potential worthwhileness and
feasibility of such ideas as may exist. Examples
of such initial studies in which MVA has been
involved are South Hampshire and Berkshire.

41.   In both of these cases, existing data
sources were used to calculate estimates of the
potential patronage of a number of alternative
Light Rail lines. The demand forecasting problem
was actually approached in three quite different
ways, looking at patronage potential first from
the view point of the residential catchment of
the lines, then the work and retail trips that
could be served, and finally estimates of the
existing volumes of movement along the corridors.
Each of these estimates was necessarily
approximate largely because only readily
available data was used. However, put together,
and given the quite different basis of
calculation of each, the alternative forecasts
allowed a consensus to be established of the
general order of magnitude of patronage likely to
be available.

42.   The order of magnitude estimates were
then used to rank schemes and options in order of
likely viability, and then to inform an overall
estimate of how likely it was that any of the
schemes could be implemented. Of course,
patronage and consequent revenue assumptions are
only part of the picture, and have to be related
to equally tentative conclusions on engineering
costs, the likelihood of there being development
opportunities which could contribute funds to
capital costs, the broad environmental and social

impacts of the scheme, and the likelihood that
congestion relief benefits could contribute to a
justification for significant Section 56 Grant.

43.   The function of these initial studies
is very much to establish whether worthwhile
possibilities exist, and to focus subsequent
examination onto the most feasible options. They
therefore provide a spring-board from which the
promoter can determine what level of resource
should be given to further exploration, if any.

Sheffield Supertram

44.   For almost three years, MVA has been
working with South Yorkshire Passenger Transport
Executive in helping move the Sheffield Supertram
proposals towards implementation. Initially
commissioned to re-appraise the viability of the
first Supertram Line in the light of the changes
brought about by bus de-regulation, MVA's demand
forecasting role has expanded to the
consideration of the Don Valley Line, as well as
advising on the demand implications of various
design issues, such as fares strategy.

45.   An essential tool in carrying out this
work has been the use of the VIPS public
transport network model. Coupled with the use of
comprehensive data on bus passenger movements,
the network model provides the scope for detailed
representation of the bus network, and its
interaction with the LRT line. Because of the
detailed operational insights that the model can
generate, it has proved ideal for simulating the
effects of alternative bus operator competitive
strategies relative to Supertram, including such
possibilities as express services, different
fares scales, and the provision of feeder
services.

46.   Because this tool was available, it was
possible to demonstrate the robustness of the
scheme, despite the uncertainties introduced by
de-regulation, and subsequently the model has
been used in an extensive program of testing,
designed to help optimise different aspects of
scheme design and the different future
assumptions. For example, fare options have been
explored at lengths, so as to illustrate the

results of policies intended to maximise Supertram fares revenue, and their implications on other aspects of scheme performance.

Manchester Metro Link

47.   With this scheme, demand forecasts have been established using rather different methods to Sheffield, reflecting different issues of data availability and circumstance, despite the apparently similar requirements.

48.   As in Sheffield, there was a need to establish the impact that de-regulation could have on estimated patronage levels and fare revenue. However, unlike Sheffield, detailed bus passenger demand data and network models were not available. Moreover, a substantial portion of initial LRT patronage was expected to come from the existing heavy rail lines serving the two corridors, which would be converted to Light Rail. Consequently, the most cost effective modelling solution was to develop explicit rail mode choice models, in which direct assumptions about the scope for bus operators to reduce service levels or fares could be directly input into the model.

49.   The mode choice models were developed using a combination of techniques, including State Preference surveys, to establish the relating weighting of different components of travel time and cost. The models were then calibrated using data on existing modal shares in each of the corridors, and incorporated into an overall modelling framework using MVA's MicroTRIPS software.

50.   The differences in approach between Sheffield and Manchester reflect the nature of the respective schemes, the availability of data, and requirements of the time. In Manchester, MVA is now undertaking further work to produce demand forecasts for extensions to the first Metro Link lines. These are likely to incorporate modelling processes similar to those used in Sheffield, although with important differences reflecting local circumstances.

CONCLUSIONS

51.   In general there are few easy solutions to transport problems, and while Light Transit systems have a role to play in improving transport in certain circumstances, then represent only some of the available solutions. Similarly, a wide range of techniques are available with which the planner can address the problem of deriving patronage forecasts, with no particular solution suiting all situations.

52.   Circumstances will tend to constrain the choice of models and data, but also the approach taken must reflect the characteristics of the individual scheme, and the requirements of the user of the forecasts.

53.   The planner needs to identify a strategy which selects the best tools for the job, and puts them together in the most cost effective way. The ideal technical solution is not necessarily the wisest choice if it involves disproportionate costs relative to the stage of the project, and jeopardises timescales. However, as a scheme progresses towards implementation, the need for reliability of the forecasts increases. Consequently, the strategy should set out how the data and models will be developed over time. In this way, the quality of information generated can make the greatest possible contribution to the success of the project as it moves from conception to implementation.

7. Finance for light, rapid transit

M. J. N. BARNETT, MA, Director, Kleinwort Benson Project
Services Ltd

SYNOPSIS. This paper outlines the perspective from which
the merchant banker views projects and explains the
functions of the financial planner and arranger. These
functions are complementary; planning precedes and is
essential to the arrangement of finance; equally planning
is useless unless arrangement follows on. Conventional and
less conventional sources of finance are discussed. The
methods of financing Light Rapid Transit systems in the
United Kingdom are noted.

FUNCTION OF THE MERCHANT BANKER.

1. Some people say that merchant bankers are
indescribable; their critics say that this is inevitable,
because they do not know what they are doing as they flit
from one thing to another. Their supporters say that it is
because merchant bankers are fleet-footed and quick-witted,
always looking for new opportunities to which to turn their
skills. Some rather more elegant expressions of these
thoughts are that merchant banks:

(a) "... owe their success to their skill in adapting to
     changing requirements and in pioneering new
     techniques",

(b)   "... cannot survive unless they remain flexible in the
      service they provide",

(c)   "... throughout nearly two centuries adapted services
      and developed advisory skills to keep abreast of
      economic and technological change",

(d)   "... refuse to be the prisoners of precedent".

PERSPECTIVE OF THE MERCHANT BANKER

2.   The perspective of merchant bankers is conditioned in
part by their own history. One strand is that of the court
banker - those who were investment adviser and arranger of
credit to monarchs and Governments, exemplified by the
funding arranged by Barings for the French reconstruction
after Waterloo. The other strand is that of the trader who
took to financing not only his own trade but that of others
too; in this group are to be found the Kleinworts and the
Bensons who, from their base in London, financed the spread
of the railroads in North and South America as an adjunct
to their trading and investment activities.

3.   Mainly from these roots has stemmed the current
business of the merchant banks:

(a)   wholesale banking
(b)   dealing in currencies and gold
(c)   corporate finance: company flotation, fund raising,
      take-overs and mergers, capital reorganization,
      privatisation, venture capital/development capital
(d)   international capital markets: issuing, underwriting,
      marketing, dealing; private placements; interest rate
      swaps, currency swaps

(e) investment management: research/share analysis;
     management of investment trusts, unit trusts, off-
     shore funds, pension funds, private client portfolios,
     trustee and personal finance planning
(f) market-making in securities
(g) miscellaneous activities: countertrade, confirming
     house, property, shipping, estate agents, commodity
     dealing, oil investment. And
(h) projects: cashflow projection, corporate structure,
     capital structure, tender preparation and assessment,
     contract negotiation, arrangement of finance.

4. There is still a great diversity between the
different houses; the business is neither standardised nor
homogeneous, but they are used to stimulating, analysing,
planning and negotiating the arrangements required by
companies and governments to finance their continuing
business and their discrete projects.

5. When acting as financial adviser on a project, the
purpose of the merchant banker is to help to ensure that

(a) the project's owner knows how much money will be
     required for capital investment and to cover operating
     costs; when it will be required; and what rate of
     return will be provided by the project revenue after
     taking into account the probable terms of finance;

(b) the owner has a practical plan for raising all the
     necessary finance and the means to put this plan into
     effect;

(c) international tenders or negotiations are undertaken
     (when appropriate) in a way which stimulates

contractors and suppliers to offer competitive prices
and terms of finance; and that competitive tenders may
then be assessed by methods which determine
comprehensively their true comparative costs;

(d) the financial and commercial aspects of the contracts
for civil construction, for equipment supply, and for
finance are satisfactorily documented.

6. In short, the banker aims to contribute to the
completion of the project 'on time and under cost.'

MEASURES OF FINANCIAL VIABILITY

7. The project owner may be unable to raise funds unless
he can show to the satisfaction of prospective investors
and lenders that the project is financially viable, because
blanket guarantees from a creditworthy government or parent
company are not forthcoming.

8. Even when the project is itself not intrinsically
viable, such an assessment may still be useful. Limited
support in the form of a capital grant, throughput
guarantee, revenue make-up provision, or some type of
subsidy - indeed anything that will decrease the risk or
increase the return - may be on offer. If so, then the
cashflow analysis can serve the dual purpose of identifying
to the owner the degree of assistance required and then to
the sources of finance that with this aid the project is
indeed viable.

9. There is no single criterion by which a banker or
investor expects to judge the commercial and financial
viability of a project. It is a combination primarily of
size - volume of funding required; timescale over which the

funding is required and can be recovered; the Internal Rate
of Return on the project itself and - more importantly - on
its equity; and the cover provided for lenders - i.e. the
ratio of the Net Present Value of future revenues available
to service debt to the value of the debt then outstanding.
It is the juxtaposition of these items, coupled with the
degree of confidence placed on them, which determines the
financial viability of a project.

10. The question of confidence is, of course, critical.
There is a degree of uncertainty inherent in the projection
of costs, revenues, terms of finance and other parameters
in the cash flow, simply because they lie in the future.
This uncertainty may often be treated with advantage by
'stochastic analysis', an iterative numerical technique
which is used to assess the possible impact upon a project
of variations of key forecast parameters from their base
values. Normally, a reasonable estimate can be made of the
range of the likely values for any of these parameters and
with a little more thought a probability of occurrence may
be assigned to each of them i.e. a frequency curve may be
constructed for each of the input variables. These
frequency curves may then be combined by using the
delightfully named Monte Carlo analysis to produce
frequency curves for the results of the cashflow
projections.

11. The outcome is that instead of producing a single
(and not particularly credible) figure for each of the main
results a range may be indicated for each result. The mean
of the results and the standard deviation - a measure of
the degree of dispersion around the mean - may then be
shown. Key features may be displayed more fully in the
form of a histogram to show the probability that any

particular value will eventuate; or as a cumulative frequency graph to show the chances that the value will exceed (or fall short of) any particular figure.

12.   Uncertainty and risk have also to be addressed in another way - risk management i.e. the identification and quantification of all the risks which are inherent in the scheme and then planning how to minimise them, control them, hive them off to others, insure them, and - in the end - accept those risks that remain as risks to the owner. One thing that the project owner has to do is to look hard at these residual risks and decide whether he can accept them. If he cannot, then the project is not feasible - or at least not for this particular owner.

13.   The analysis of cashflows and risks is matched with an assessment of the best corporate structure - ie. appropriate debt: equity ratio; public and/or private sector ownership; private or publicly quoted company or unincorporated joint venture; relationship of the promoter with the main constructors and suppliers and the nature of their contracts.

14.   Owner and financial adviser will also have taken care to present the case for the project and the way it is to be financed to local government, central government (eg. the Departments of Transport ["DTp"] and Environment, Cabinet Office and No 10 Policy Unit), and Parliament, as necessary. The maintenance of such relationships is all part of the job of ensuring that the project is in touch with the real world.

15.   Only when every piece of the jig-saw is in place can the funds be subscribed and the project go ahead.

CONVENTIONAL FINANCE

16.   In recent decades rail transport systems in the UK
have tended to be funded by the public sector. Apart from
direct investment by government bodies, at least three
other public sector sources merit a mention.

17.   Central Government. Under the provisions of Section
56 of the Transport Act 1968, grants for up to 50% of the
capital cost of a suitable project may be provided by the
DTp; this amount has to be matched by the relevant Local
Authority. A recent redefinition of the conditions of the
grant requires that benefits gained by travellers on the
system are paid for by those travellers or from yet other
sources of funds. Section 56 funds may not exceed the non-
user benefits - typically decongestion of the roads, but
possibly including cost savings for British Rail, reduction
in parking and garage space requirements, employment
generation and environmental benefits - on which the
influence of the Pearce report has yet to be seen.

18.   European Regional Development Fund ["ERDF"]. ERDF
grants are aimed primarily at the poorest community
countries - Greece, Spain, Portugal and Ireland. Their
take-up tends to be restricted by the fact that funds have
to be matched 50:50 by the host government. Therefore,
substantial grants are available to 'assisted areas' in the
richer countries. In the U.K. these are channelled through
the Department of the Environment.

19.   European Investment Bank ["EIB"]. The EIB's
involvement in financing major transport infrastructure
in the Community has been extended to urban transport
schemes which reduce traffic congestion and resultant
energy waste and environmental pollution. EIB is

accustomed to providing long-term finance for up to one-
half of the capital cost of a project. The funds may be
denominated in sterling at a fixed rate of interest which
reflects the market conditions to EIB i.e. the finest
terms. The degree of project risk acceptable to the EIB is
determined on a case-by-case basis. When required, a
commercial banking syndicate might provide a limited form
of guarantee to EIB in lieu of providing all or a portion
of the loan funds.

20.   In recent years and in accordance with the political
philosophy of Mrs Thatcher's administrations, government
has tended to require promoters to maximise private sector
funding before making available public funds.

21.   Equity. The volume of equity which can be attracted
to the project will depend on the projected return, on
the degree of risk that this return is not eventually
achievable, and on other benefits that may attach to
parties with ancillary interests. Equity will initially be
subscribed by the owners, by others with a commercial
interest in the project - possibly contractors and
suppliers; and by venture capitalists who accept a high
degree of project risk and expect a commensurately high
rate of return and the possibility of realising the
investment within five years. If the risks can be shown to
be well contained, financial institutions may be willing to
inject equity for the long term and at rather more modest
rates. For the largest and soundest projects, a public
flotation may be necessary and practicable. (Note that
equity is intrinsically expensive but usually essential;
the success of the Dartford River Crossing company in
raising £160 million on the back of £1,000 equity will not
be easy to emulate).

22. <u>Mezzanine Finance</u>. Preference shares, convertible
bonds, bonds with warrants and a number of other
instruments with some of the characteristics of equity may
be useful on occasion. Long term loans at fixed rates of
interest may be available from financial institutions - for
instance pension funds and insurance companies.

23. <u>Bank loans</u>. Loans from banks tend to be at floating
rates of interest and to extend to 12-15 years at most.
They have the three great advantages that

*   banks are used to projects, so they are flexible and
        within reason willing to tailor the terms to the needs
        of the project;

*   large amounts are available;

*   the banks are always there. Other markets are more
        volatile and can dry up completely for extended
        periods.

24. **Leasing**. Under current UK tax rules, the owner can
claim capital allowances for the cost of rolling stock and
other equipment on the basis of a 25% reducing balance, and
may offset these allowances against corporation tax
payable. However, given the imbalance between the cost of
the rolling stock and equipment and the profit in the early
years of the typical project, it may well prove more
efficient to pass on the capital allowances via an
equipment leasing scheme and to accumulate the benefit by
way of reduced funding costs. When the project risk is
unacceptable to prospective lessors, letters of credit from
a bank or syndicate of banks may be arranged to cover their
risk.

LESS CONVENTIONAL FINANCE

25. Property. When in the nineteenth century the Metropolitan Railway Company was building its lines out from London into the country, it also set up an organisation to promote estate development in the vicinity of the railway. More land than was needed for operational purposes was acquired and this was disposed of eventually for building purposes. At that time little thought was given to selling the land for profit in an attempt to fund the railway; its purpose was to control the speed and location of development along the railway, and thus to increase the patronage on the railway itself. However, there are a number of methods by which an urban transport system may attempt to obtain additional profit or funds for finance from real estate development and the enhancement of land values.

26. Air space utilization is a concept which has been extensively developed in the US, Europe, Australia, and also in cities in Asia. Development may take either of two forms - the value of the air space may be recognised in the first instance by joint venture development, or air space uses may be added as the need further to develop scarce land arises, an example of which is commercial development above railway tracks and termini.

27. 'Excess condemnation' is the jargon for the purchase of more land than is strictly required for the transport system itself. It is popular in North America but may be of less interest in areas of high property density or where the legal position is less favourable.

28. Efforts may be made to persuade developers and property owners to make a cash contribution to the cost of

a new or improved transport system which will enhance their property. Historically, developers have not usually been willing to recognise such benefit; smaller developers in particular have tended to take a free ride, on the view that the decision whether the project goes ahead will not be affected by any contribution from them. It is difficult to make such a scheme work unless there is a single massive development whose developers can be persuaded that the transport project will not go ahead in the absence of a substantial contribution.

29. Taxation. If a new transport system increases the value of adjacent properties, then there is a reasonable argument not only for an increase in the local property taxes but also that some part of these taxes should be allotted directly to the transport system itself. In some countries this concept of an 'improvement tax' is well enshrined in law. Typically, the relevant area is divided into concentric circles around the stations or boarding points, with the effective tax decreasing as distance from the station increases. In some cases the method includes the greater sophistication of differing grades of 'benefit'. For example, general economic, environmental and social advantages are to be gained by all property owners; then there is the increase in value of residential property in the 'zones of influence' of the stations; and then again there are the specific advantages to be obtained by commercial firms in these zones. Suprisingly little serious research using rigorous statistical and scientific methods has been conducted into the effect of transport systems on the value of adjacent property values.

30. Several authorities have proposed the establishment of a payroll tax. Employers would be required to

contribute a proportion of their payroll towards local
transport improvements. A precedent exists in Paris, where
all companies employing more than ten people pay 1% of
their payroll to a fund destined for investment in public
transport.

31. Another proposal is the hypothecation (anathema to
the Treasury) of road licence or fuel tax revenues. For
this there is a precedent in Germany.

INDIVIDUAL TOWNS AND CITIES

32. Other conference papers will have listed the many
towns and cities in the UK which have pretensions to a
Light Rapid Transit. Most of these are looking for some
mix of public and private sector finance. Even socialist
local authorities recognise the need to work with the
private sector in current circumstances; and even the
fervent private sector promoters of the ATA in Bristol
decided eventually to seek a Section 56 grant. This apart,
the schemes·are characterised by their heterogeneity in
terms of size and sponsor as well as technically,
politically, commercially and financially. Many of the
systems - for instance, West Midlands, South Yorkshire and
Avon - are currently in a rapid stage of development and
comment may better be reserved for March 1990. Comment on
the three systems most advanced - in time - may be merited.

33. Tyne and Wear. This pioneer of LRT in the UK
succeeded in obtaining full central and local government
funding after a particularly professional campaign in the
mid 70's. The first extension from Bankfoot to the airport
is to be financed primarily from the farebox, the reserves
and capital receipts of the PTE and a contribution from the

airport; at the time of writing applications are in hand
for grants from the EEC and Section 56. Further
development to Washington and Sunderland is under
consideration; decision on the type and mix of public and
private funds is some way away.

34. London Docklands Light Railway. The first route,
commissioned in 1987, was financed by central government
only after considerable discussion of the possibilities of
finance from the GLC and from the private sector. The
short but expensive extension from Tower Hill to Bank is
also being funded by central government but in this case
with a £67 million grant from Olympia and York, recognising
the value of this extension to their development at
Canary Wharf. A further extension eastwards to Becton is
to be financed by the London Docklands Development
Corporation, largely from the proceeds of the sale of land
the value of which will be enhanced by the extension. (The
extension of the Jubilee Line via Waterloo to the Isle of
Dogs and onwards is not strictly a light transit but the
bargaining between the DTp and Olympia and York as to
whether it was to be a public sector railway with a
contribution from the private sector, or vice versa, and in
either case the size of the contribution is of some
interest. At the time of writing it has been settled that
London Regional Transport will be the promoter but the size
and conditions of the Olympia and York grant have not been
declared.)

35. Manchester Metrolink. After several years' study
and negotiation with the European Community and DTp, and
after holding a tender competition for private sector
consortia, in September 1989 the Manchester PTE awarded a
contract for the design, construction, operation and

maintenance of Phase 1 of Metrolink - connecting Bury with
Altrincham via a City Centre link. The consortia were
required to bid for the value of the one-off grant required
for them to accept the above obligations, finance the
balance of the capital cost and the entire operating cost,
and receive the revenues from the system for a period of 15
years. At the time of writing the size of the grant (to be
met 50:50 from Section 56 and by the local authorities) has
not been made public, and neither has the the method by
which the winning GMA consortium will fund its share of the
cost. The nature of the contract between the PTE and GMA
and the way in which near-term and more distant extensions
to the system will be managed will also be of interest.

Discussion on papers 5 – 7

J. GLOVER, <u>Colin Buchanan & Partners</u>
Mr Tyson emphasized the need to maximize revenue from users.
What effect will this have on charging systems; what will be
the effects on users and demand? As a result of the Lewisham
extension of the DLR, according to Mr Collins (Paper 3,
paragraph 34) passengers can avoid travelling via Central
London. Thus, using the London Travelcard, they will avoid
Zone 1 and pay perhaps one-third less for a journey from
Bexleyheath to Canary Wharf. How can such problems be
resolved?

W. J. TYSON, <u>Paper 5</u>
The specific example of Docklands shows that, for whatever
mode, the London Regional Transport zonal fares system is
designed for journeys to central London only. In time I
believe it will have to be modified to take account of cross-
London movement. In general there will be great pressure for
innovative charging systems and I would see more emphasis
being placed on fares structures and payment methods in
future.

J. FEARON, <u>Transportation Planning Association</u>
TPA experience in London and the West Midlands leads us to
believe that the key features of LRT demand models are as
follows

(a)   a modelling system which allows quick and efficient
      sensitivity and option testing
(b)   a modelling system which allows the integration of
      public transport and highway network models for Section
      56 grant studies.

The solution, we believe, is the advanced EMME/2 suite,
which has been used for recent studies of the DLR, the
Midlands Metrolink one Section 56 study and the Central London
Rail Study.

DISCUSSION

A. LAST, Paper 6

MVA's experience, as referred to in the Paper, is that no
single planning package is likely to have all the features
necessary to carry a Light Transit scheme from inception
through to implementation. While there is a place for
strategic models such as EMME/2, it is likely that the
financial and economic justification of a scheme will demand
models able to operate at a greater level of detail. For
example, measurement of decongestion benefits (and
disbenefits) may require modelling of individual junction
delays on the highway network. Equally, the need for robust
revenue forecasts is best satisfied by a model incorporating a
detailed representation of different fare systems.

F. K. SMITH, Ove Arup & Partners

The importance of taking into account the requirements of
the users of systems should not be underestimated. This does
not appear to have been addressed by Mr Last's paragraphs 11
and 12. How are users' needs being taken into account when
undertaking demand forecasts?

On the question of risk management and financial planning, I
wonder if Mr Barnett could tell us how the financial risk of
the parliamentary bill process can be quantified.

A. LAST, Paper 6

Mr Smith's question highlights the fact that without
passengers, transit systems are of course redundant. All who
are concerned with promoting a public transport system should
have that fact uppermost in their minds. The implication is
that demand forecasts should be based on solid consumer
research, which can be used both to establish a basis of fact
concerning present travel behaviour, and also to allow changes
in behaviour to be soundly predicted. Surveys and model
building are thus essential parts of the process by which
planners can ensure that users' needs are taken into account.

M. J. N. BARNETT, Paper 7

I have only strictly limited experience of insuring against
the risk of a parliamentary bill failing. This leads me to
suggest that such insurance is expensive and the causes for
claim strictly limited. However, others present may have
wider experience.

G. SAPSTEAD, Minet Trans Risk Services Ltd

With reference to Mr Barnett's comment that he believed
limited insurance had been taken out in the past for
protection against the failure of a Parliamentary Bill, I can
confirm that cover is now available not only for failure of a

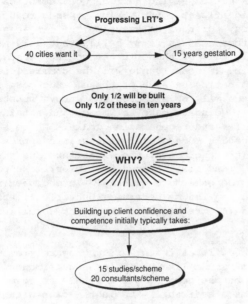

Figure 1

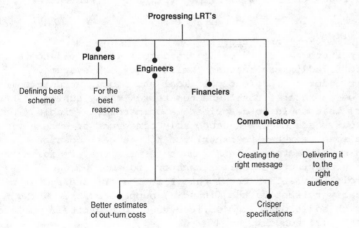

Figure 2

DISCUSSION

Private Bill, but also amendment and delay of the Bill in its
passage through both Houses.

P. VERNON, Mott MacDonald
Of the 40 UK cities giving serious consideration to LRTs
today, as a significant contribution towards reducing
congestion today, or towards securing the city-centre
regeneration tomorrow, it is my belief that only half will be
built, and only half of those in the coming decade. Why is
this? Typically 20 consultants will be commissioned over a 15
year gestation period on each of these. But more importantly
this performance will be expected to improve substantially if
LRTs are really going to make an impact and attain these
congestion-relief and regeneration goals. These studies
increasingly need a more closely integrated approach between
the planners, the engineers, the financiers and the
communicators. And clients need a slicker, more penetrating
and endurable response more quickly. In engineering we are
addressing two key issues here: (a) better estimating of out-
turn costs and (b) creating more relevant specifications.

W. J. TYSON, Paper 5
Lack of finance is an issue - if aggregate promoters'
aspirations do exceed likely funding requirements. We are
also hampered by the need to get a scheme approved before any
funds can be made available - as is the case with Sheffield
Supertram which is effectively on the 'waiting list'. A
commitment to a public transport investment programme similar
to the roads programme is needed from the Government.

P. DAWKINS, Merz and McLellan
The private sector is being urged to promote, finance and
operate fixed infrastructure public transport systems.
However under the present political and social structure in
which we operate, I doubt whether there is any scheme in the
country that could be described as commercially viable. Not
until our roads become unacceptably congested or such a time
as the road user has to contribute to the real cost of
providing the motoring infrastructure will the provision of
fixed infrastructure public transport schemes become
commercially viable. Until that time the private sector will
be totally reliant on the financial support of the public
sector in addition to the obvious need to have their political
and technical support.

W. J. TYSON, Paper 5
The link between user charges for roads and the demand for
public transport will assume greater importance in the future
unless direct road user charging is ruled out politically.

8. Light, heavy or innovative? A review of current systems

G. HOWARD, BSc (Eng), MRAeS, Transit Systems Manager, Kennedy Henderson Limited

SYNOPSIS. Building new urban railways using existing heavy rail technology has become increasingly difficult in recent years because of their high costs and environmental implications. Alternative technologies have become available, particularly where peak demand ranges from 10,000 to 20,000 passengers an hour. This paper describes some of these available and illustrates them with examples of well developed systems.

INTRODUCTION

1. Urban railways have traditionally employed heavy rail technology, whether they ran elevated, at-grade, or underground. In recent years few urban areas have been able to contemplate introducing totally new heavy urban rail systems, with a very small number of notable exceptions. The capital costs tend to put such systems out of the financial reach of all but the most economically prosperous areas: the disruption to the urban fabric envisaged during construction can cause powerful objections on environmental grounds, as well as from those with the responsibility for maintaining the flow of road traffic: the expectation that continuing public subsidy will be required to operate the system leads to concerns being expressed by local tax-payers through their elected representatives: and, in many cases, the existing public transport operators have become so conditioned by years of falling patronage that their self-confidence in providing a major new system has been severely eroded.

2. This has led to alternative types of system being considered for urban railways, employing other than the traditional technologies. Some of these systems are derived from heavy rail technology (for example light rail transit), others (guided buses) are derived from an obviously different technology, while others (such as magnetic levitation) employ their own technology.

3.   Despite this, most of these systems share a common objective. This is to offer an attractive public transport service on corridors where the demand is such that road transport cannot cope without unacceptable environmental or economic effects, yet the demand is not great enough to support a traditional heavy rail system. Typically, such levels of demand range from less than 10,000 to more than 20,000 passengers an hour during the peak, whereas a 40000+ is now widely thought to be necessary to warrant a heavy urban railway.

4.   The alternative types of system available to meet the lower levels of demand are discussed in the following sections, with some illustrative examples.

ALTERNATIVE TYPES OF SYSTEM
Major differences
5.   Generally the difference between the various types relates to the support and guidance technology and the degree of automatic operation offered. These areas are discussed in the following paragraphs.

Basic types of support and guidance
6.   There are basically three types of support which may be used. These are:

Steel wheel on steel rail

Rubber tyred wheel on concrete, steel or timber track

Magnetic levitation on steel reaction rail.

7.   There are many examples of steel wheeled and rubber tyred wheeled vehicles in routine operation throughout the world. Magnetic levitation, which has been developed particularly in Germany and Japan, and latterly in the USA and UK, has reached an advanced stage and many development installations are operating under test conditions. The "people mover" at Birmingham National Exhibition Centre is the only example of a low-speed installation in public service.

Steel wheeled vehicles
8.   The history of the steel wheel dates from the early nineteenth century. It was originally adopted, running on a fixed track to provide an alternative to wooden wheels running on poor quality roads, with consequent reduction in rolling resistance and an improvement in riding qualities. Early flanged tracks with lateral guidance surfaces for

cylindrical wheels were soon superseded by shaped rails and the wheels were flanged to provide guidance.

9.   The steel wheel not only provides support and guidance for the vehicles, but by the use of low voltage circuits which include rails, wheels and axles enables vehicles to be detected continuously either stationery or moving, providing the basis for a safe signalling system. In the case of electric traction, the rails also carry the return current, so that only one additional conductor (in the case of DC or single phase AC) is required.

Rubber tyred vehicles
10.   The rubber tyred wheel, and particularly the pneumatic tyred wheel, is a later invention than the steel wheel. With the advent of macadamised road surfaces and the internal combustion engine, it brought to road transport smoother riding qualities and much reduced rolling resistance, although this is still greater than with a steel wheel. For nearly sixty years development of the rubber tyred vehicle was restricted to road transport, and the flexibility associated with the road vehicle eroded the supremacy of steel wheeled railways in both passenger and freight transport.

11.   In the 1950's the suspension equipment of all rail vehicles consisted of combinations of leaf and coil steel springs, and, compared with rubber tyred road vehicles the ride was both noisier and less comfortable. In order to introduce the benefits of the rubber tyre to railways, the Paris Metro built trains with rubber tyres, to run on existing lines. These required additional tracks for the rubber tyres to run on, and horizontal rubber tyred wheels are fitted to the bogies which make contact with new guide beams to steer the bogies. Other complications included the need for steel flanged wheels to guide the train through junctions and give support in the event of a puncture, and separate traction current return conductors.

12.   A number of manufacturers have developed rubber-tyred monorail systems. These either are suspended from an overhead guideway (Siemens-Duewag, and Messerschmidt-Bolkow-Blohm) or straddle a guidebeam (Universal Mobility, Rohr, Wedway, Von Roll.) These were all conceived as overhead systems.

13.   The suspended systems tend to be uneconomic for operation in tunnels because the height required for the vehicle and its guideway is significantly greater than for conventional bottom supported vehicles. For example, the MBB

C-Bahn system requires some 4 metres for the cabin and bogie. Also their cabins are small; the largest carry some 50 passengers only.

14. Many of those which straddle a beam have been developed for amusement parks. As a consequence they operate at low speeds, with maximum speeds at less than 30 km/h. and, generally, are unsuitable for the heavy use experienced in public transport service. However, the Von Roll system has been developed for public transport use and a system has been installed in Sydney, Australia.

15. Some twenty years ago, a number of manufacturers who had no previous railway experience, entered the personal rapid transit (PRT) field, mainly in the USA. This resulted in the building of a number of trial installations consisting essentially of small cabins supported on four rubber tyred wheels, and guided (or steered) by various devices. All these installations included fully automatic, no-man operation and the height of the guides presented barriers to any person or vehicle wishing to cross the track. They therefore could not be used for street work and were confined to elevated routes. Most of the manufacturers initially interested gave up when the personal rapid transit concept failed to gain acceptance, but a few (notably Westinghouse Electric) persisted and increased the size of vehicle to group rapid transit size (40-100 passengers). A number of installations are now in operation, mainly at airports in the USA although two are now operational at Gatwick Airport, and the systems is employed for the Miami Downtown component of Metro Rail.

16. A later development is the guided bus. This was first introduced by Mercedes-Benz who equipped a conventional, diesel powered, bus which may be driven normally or guided by small, horizontal wheels which was against small guidewalls on either side. A later development offered electric traction from an overhead wire. This system was initially installed on a demonstration track in Essen in West Germany and a public, system was installed in Adelaide in Australia. The concept was extended by BN of Belgium who developed its GLT system. This is a double articulated bus which may be driven normally or guided by a wheel running on a central rail. Its primary means of traction is electric, drawing power from an overhead wire but it is also fitted with a diesel engine for independent operation.

Magnetic levitation
17. Magnetic levitation systems have been developed in

recent years aimed at low and high (300 km/h plus) speed applications.

18. <u>Suspension.</u> There are two systems of magnetic levitation; the electro- magnetic system and the electro-dynamic system. In the electro- magnetic system the vehicle is fitted with electro-magnets. Because electro-magnets can only generate an attractive force they are located below suspension rails and support the vehicle by upward attraction. The system is inherently unstable and so the gap between the magnets and suspension rails and magnetic flux within it are measured constantly and fed back to adjust the current in the windings of the magnet to maintain the gap at a sensibly constant height. In order to maintain the efficiency of the magnetic circuit, the gap is kept to a small value, typically less than 30 mm maximum. This effectively limits the amount of suspension movement available and can give poor ride quality of higher speeds. This can be overcome by introducing a secondary suspension between the chassis frame carrying the magnets and the passenger compartment. Losses occur in the suspension rails as a result of the changing polarity as the north and south poles of the magnet traverse the rail as the vehicle moves. This manifests itself as a significant drag force which increases with speed. The losses can be reduced by using laminated suspension rails.

19. In the electro-dynamic system the vehicle is fitted with powerful electro-magnets, which are generally super cooled to a very low temperature in order to reduce their losses to an acceptable level. When these magnets move over a metal plate they set up eddy currents which react with the magnetic field to generate a repulsive force. Generation of this force depends on there being relative movement between the magnets and the guideway so there can be no levitating force when the vehicle is at rest. Because of this the vehicles are fitted with wheels and it is only when the vehicle has accelerated to the appropriate speed that it levitates and takes off. Because of this characteristic, electro-dynamic systems are not suitable to application to low or medium speed systems.

20. <u>Propulsion.</u> Non-contacting propulsion systems are used to complement the non- contacting suspension system. A linear motor is invariably used.

21. A linear motor consists of a stator and a reaction rail. The stator is the active part of the motor consisting of windings which are supplied with a three phase electric power. The reaction rail is the passive part of the motor

and consists of an aluminium strip backed by an iron rail. There are two types of linear motor; the short stator and the long stator.

22.   In the short stator motor, the stator is carried on the vehicle and the reaction rail forms part of the track or guideway. The vehicle picks up electrical power though pick-up shoes from a wayside conductor rail and the vehicle is controlled by its on-board equipment.

23.   In the long stator motor the situation is reversed. The passive reaction rail is carried on the vehicle and the wound stator extends the entire length of the track. The stator is sectioned and each section may be electrically powered from wayside equipment. Although extending the stator the entire length of the track in the long stator system is costly, it obviates the need to transfer power to the vehicle which can cause difficulties at very high speeds. Also the progress of the vehicles can be controlled from the wayside with no need to transmit control information and data to and from the vehicles.

24.   Magnetically levitated vehicles have been developed in Great Britain, Germany and Japan, but only one (a low speed electro- magnetically levitated system) has been introduced into public service. This is a twin track system connecting the Terminal Building and Railway Station and Birmingham International Airport in Great Britain. The vehicles carry 44 passengers and are limited to shuttling to and fro as no switch has been developed. The design maximum speed is 47 km/h.

Automation of operation
25.   Traditionally rail systems employed manual operation of the vehicles, with the option of automatic or preprogrammed route setting and signalling. Overall control can be exercised from a central control room by regulating the service through intervention on the signalling system and by radio contact with drivers. Where unsegregated running for light rail systems is required it is obviously necessary for manual on-sight operation of the vehicle to be retained. For partially segregated systems a combination of on sight driving and colour light signalling is acceptable

26.   It is possible to fit Automatic Vehicle Operation (AVO) equipment to a light rail vehicle so that the vehicle is driven automatically between stations. The driver only is responsible for initiating the starting sequence (Docklands, Victoria Line, Hong Kong, etc.). By further automation the doors can be opened and closed and the vehicle started on

schedule without human intervention (BART San Francisco) to give fully automatic or no-person operation. However no-person operation has implications for the safety and security of the system and has rarely been adopted for this reason, in general urban public transport service. It is however used for airport transit links where its usage can be more closely supervised.

27.   The rubber tyred guided installations, on the other hand, were conceived from the start as fully automated systems. The proprietary systems offered were developed from the personal rapid transit concept, where the principle of operation was to give near private car or taxi privacy and service. One fundamental advantage of the rubber tyred vehicle for this type of operation, with service frequencies reckoned in seconds rather than minutes, is its high adhesion offering very high emergency braking rates. (Normal braking rates are similar to those of steel wheeled vehicles due to constraints of passenger comfort.) Even with larger vehicles this advantage is exploited in enabling units to operate scheduled services, stopping at all stations at frequencies of 1 minute. Even then the cost of such cars is high in proportion to their size compared with standard LRT cars.

28.   The advantages and disadvantages of AVO are:

(a)   All vehicles (or trains) conform to the same performance pattern, optimising both energy consumption and line capacity. But energy consumption and line capacity can be optimised only if station dwell time is rigorously controlled and an "intelligent" AVO system is employed which can monitor the state of the track ahead further than one track circuit.

(b)   Repetitive automatic operation of equipment precludes driver error thereby reducing maintenance and repair costs. However the repetitive nature of the operation can in fact increase maintenance and repair costs due to exact positioning of current collection equipment during station stops, introduction of hard spots into overhead lines, and increase in rail corrugation due to repetition of train movement pattern.

(c)   Where it is desired to operate one person trains in single track tunnels, the UK Railway Inspectorate desires Automatic Vehicle Operation as a safety requirement. The reason for this is to ensure a vehicle is not stranded between stations should the

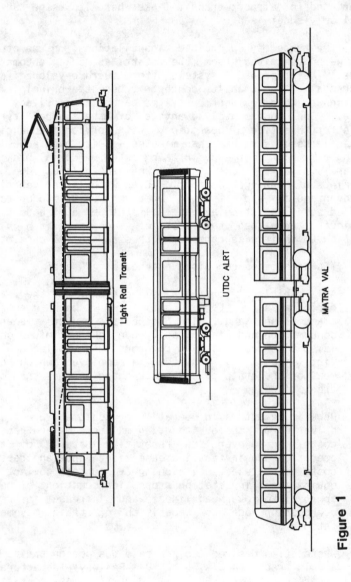

Light Rail Transit

UTDC ALRT

MATRA VAL

Figure 1

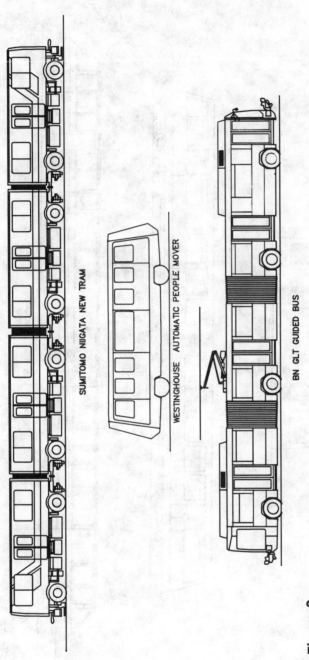

SUMITOMO NIIGATA NEW TRAM

WESTINGHOUSE AUTOMATIC PEOPLE MOVER

BN GLT GUIDED BUS

Figure 2

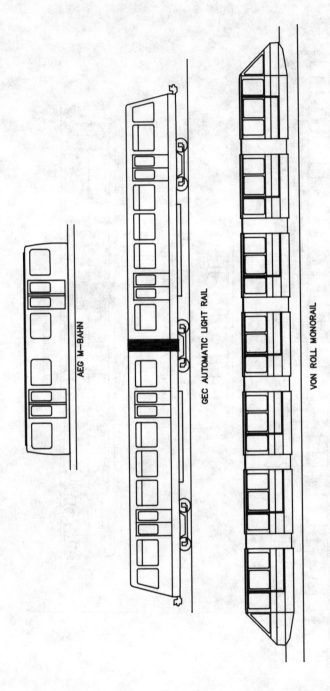

AEG M—BAHN

GEC AUTOMATIC LIGHT RAIL

VON ROLL MONORAIL

Figure 3

driver collapse when no second person is available to take over control. Experience of this type of operation elsewhere does not endorse the requirement on statistical grounds.

(d)   It is the first step to no-person vehicle operation and can be considered as a transitional phase. This is especially true where automation of station duties (door operation, despatch) is provided. Automatic Train Operation has been in existence for almost 20 years on a regular basis. No railway yet has moved to no-person operation.

(e)   Even if it is intended to retain an operator on board for safety or passenger service reasons, automatic operation allows him to patrol the vehicle, collect fares or check tickets and generally assist passengers. However in this case full segregation is essential to avoid the need to monitor the track ahead. If the line is operated as a fully automated system, with the operator having no set driving functions except in emergency, then on board fare collection with one person may be feasible without delaying vehicles/trains at station whilst fares are collected.

TYPICAL SYSTEMS
    29.   The characteristics of the of some of the types of system are described in the following sections. There are a number of manufacturers offering steeled-wheeled light rail transit systems and, with the exception of UTDC, they may be regarded as the same type of system, generally known as LRT. These systems all have very similar characteristics and a typical example may taken as illustrative of this type. However, this is not the case for other systems. Each of these has been developed by a different manufacturer; they contain patentable and proprietary concepts and are totally individual.

Light Rail Transit
    30.   Light Rail Transit (LRT) systems are fully developed and in service in many towns and cities worldwide. Their applications range from on street operation using small vehicles (100 passenger) through to fully segregated operation with large vehicles (200 + passengers). LRT uses steel wheeled articulated vehicles propelled by rotary traction motors which normally collect power from an overhead wire at up to 750V dc. Vehicles are usually manually driven although automatic driving is possible. A larger single

articulated vehicle is typically 27 m long and 2.65 m wide with four bi-parting doors 1.6 m wide on each side which are used for normal and emergency access and egress. A typical configuration would provide 72 seats and room for up to 140 standing passengers, each occupying $0.2m^2$. The body is usually of light welded steel construction with integration of main equipment cases, cable ducts, and air ducting into the main structural elements. Large windows, fluorescent lighting, and insulated walls contribute to passenger comfort.

31.   Vehicles run on conventional railway track of 1435mm gauge. For segregated operations conventional railway rails and turnouts may be used, although grooved rail and special turnouts are need for street running.

32.   LRT offers a well proven technology which has been developed over many years in many countries.

UTDC - ALRT
33.   The Advanced Light Rapid Transit (ALRT) system has been developed by the Urban Transportation Development Corporation of Canada. It has been conceived as a complete system incorporating vehicle, guideway, control system, power supply etc. It has been extensively developed in Canada, culminating in extensive running on UTDC' test track. Orders were placed for three revenue- earning installations in Vancouver, Scarborough (Canada) and Detroit (USA) with an expected initial production run of 76 vehicles. Revenue service began in 1986 in Vancouver and in 1985 in Scarborough. In Detroit revenue service began in 1987. The ALRT system uses steel wheeled vehicles propelled by linear electric motors. Power is supplied through low level conductor rails at 600V dc and no-person operation is possible using the SELTRAC automatic control system. ALRT vehicles are 12.7 m long by 2.5 m wide, and have two bi-parting doors, 1.22 m wide on each side. End doors permit emergency egress and maintenance access. A typical configuration has 28 perimeter seats at 0.41 sq m per passenger, and space for 58 standing passengers each occupying 0.20 sq m. Wheelchairs may also be accommodated.

34.   Conventional railway track is used, although in the interests of low maintenance a heavy (115lb) rail section has been employed. The reaction rail for the LIM consists of an aluminium sheet backed by iron underneath and is fastened between the two running rails.

Matra - VAL
35.   After a development period of 10 years and a 12

months period of full service test running, the first example
of the Matra system opened for public revenue service in 1983
at Lille in France. In 1985 the City of Toulouse decided to
adopt the system, and in 1986 Jacksonville signed a contract
to use VAL for its downtown connection, and a contract was
signed for a system at Chicago O'Hare airport. The cities of
Strasbourg and Bordeaux decided in favour of Val, which was
also selected for the connection to Paris Orly airport.   In
1988 the city of Taipei adopted VAL for part of its
underground network.   The VAL system uses electrically
propelled driverless vehicles with rubber tyred wheels
running on segregated concrete guideways. Electric power is
collected from low level conductor rails at 750V dc which
also act as guide rails, and the system is fully automatic,
controlled from a central facility.   The original system at
Lille is now known as VAL206 and is the only one in service.
The number indicates the vehicle width in centimetres. The
original VAL-206 has to run in married pairs, but Matra have
designed a vehicle, VAL206-S capable of running singly.   For
Jacksonville and Chicago O'Hare airport a wider vehicle, the
VAL256, has been designed. The vehicles are 28 m long and
2.56 m wide. 4 externally sliding doors each 2.13 m wide are
provided on each side of the pair of cars. 48 seats are
provided together with space for 150 standing passengers at
5/sq m.   Wheel chairs can be accommodated.

36.   Running surfaces comprise two reinforced concrete
beams 5.2 m long which are bolted to the concrete base. A
special coating is used on elevated structures to give
optimum adhesion in wet conditions.   Lateral guidance is
provided by two steel H beams located on each side of the
guideway. These beams are carried on insulators because they
also act as conductor rails.

37.   The Matra system is a fully integrated system
developed over a long period of time which has achieved 5
years of public passenger carrying service, and has now
received orders for further installations.

Sumitomo/Niigata - New Tram
38.   The New Tram system has been developed by Niigata
Engineering Company of Japan.   Development began in 1969 and,
following an extensive development programme, was selected in
1977 for the 6.6 km connection between Suminoekoen and
Nakafuto in Osaka Nanko.   Construction began in 1978 and was
completed in 1981. It uses technology licensed from the
Vought Corporation of the USA who developed the Airtrans
system serving Dallas/Fort Worth airport which entered
service in 1974.   The New Tram system uses electrically
propelled automatically driven vehicles running on rubber

tyres on a segregated concrete guideway. Power is collected
from low level conductor rails at 600V 3-phase ac and,
although the system is capable of fully automatic operation,
a driver is carried on each train. Vehicles operate in
trains of four (two units of two vehicles). Each vehicle is
7.6 m long and 2.29 m wide. One double leaf sliding door is
provided on each side of the vehicle. 22 longitudinal seats
are provided with space for 35 standing passengers at $0.2m^2$
each. This gives a total train capacity of 228 passengers.
The body is made of weather proof steel. Windows are fixed
and the vehicle is air-conditioned for the comfort of
passengers. The vehicles forming a train are connected to
enable passengers to more freely from one vehicle to another.

39. The guideway consists of a concrete structure,
typically 7.4 m wide for double track, with raised concrete
side walks 1 m length. The vehicle runs on raised concrete
running surfaces. Lateral guidance is provided by
guidewheels running on steel guide rails attached to the
sidewalls on plain track.

40. The New Tram is a fully integrated system developed
over a long period. It uses technology developed for the
Dallas/Fort Worth Airtrans system which entered service in
1974 after several years of development.

AEG-Westinghouse - Automated People Mover
41. The Automated People Mover has been developed by
Westinghouse Electric Corporation of the USA and has been
installed at Atlanta, Orlando, Seattle-Tacoma, Tampa and
Miami airports in the USA and two installations at Gatwick
airport in the UK. It also forms the Down Town component of
the Miami Metro Rail system. The Automated People Mover uses
small rubber tyred vehicles propelled by rotary electric
motors. Power is collected from low level conductor rails
mounted centrally at 600V 3-phase ac. The system operates
fully automatically. The Automated People Mover vehicles are
12.75 m long and have two bi- parting doors, 2.13 m wide. No
separate emergency egress is provided. a typical
configuration has 28 seated passengers and 54 standing each
occupying 0.2 m/2. Wheelchairs can be accommodated.

42. The trackwork required consists of two concrete
running surfaces together with a central steel guide beam and
supports for the conductor rails. The concrete running
surfaces have to be designed and constructed within a
tolerance of 3 mm in 3 m. In some cases it is necessary to
grind the guideway to achieve this tolerance. The steel
superstructure may be supported on steel or reinforced
concrete piers on elevated sections. For at grade track an

entirely concrete guideway may be laid. Turnouts comprise
two sections of the central guide beam, one straight and one
curved, which operate in unison with one section pivoting
into position while the other pivots out of the way.

43.   The Westinghouse Automated People Mover is probably
the most highly developed fully automatic system available.
However it has only been used on relatively simple shuttle
links in the protected environment of airports, except for
the Down Town component of the Miami Metro Rail system.

BN - GLT guided bus
44.   Guided Light Transit System has been developed by
BN (formerly La Brugeoise et Nivelles) of Belgium following a
9 year development programme. It is in service at at initial
installation at Rochefort in Belgium. The GLT uses rubber
tyred vehicles developed from convention bus technology. It
can be driven on the road under the power of its on-board
diesel engine and also on a dedicated guideway under the
power of its on-board electric motors which draw power from
an overhead wire. The GLT vehicle is 25.3m long and 2.5m
wide. It has 4 bi-parting doors on either side. No separate
doors for emergency egress are provided. The passenger
accomodation is 72 seated and 98 standing at $5/m^2$. Wheel
chairs cannot be accomodated because of the high floor and
steps at the entrance.

45.   For street running the vehicle is manually driven
from the front using conventional controls; steering wheel,
pedals etc. For guided operation small double flanged guide
wheels mounted on the centreline of the vehicle are lowered
to engage with a railway rail whose top is set flush with the
running surface and with grooves on either side to accomodate
the flanges of the guidewheels. All axles are steered to
allow the vehicle to negotiate 12m radius curves in both its
modes of operation.

46.   On the guided sections only the additional trackwork
required is a single railway section rail located in the
centre of each track. Where the tracks may be used by other
road vehicles the rail must be set flush with the running
surface. If the track is dedicated to the GLT system then
the guideway may be lowered between the running surfaces and
the guiderail allowed to stand proud. Raised wing rails are
used to direct the guide wheels onto the guide rail on the
approach to guided sections. Switching is achieved using
conventional railway technology to move a section of the
guide rail to direct the vehicle on the desired route.

47.   The BN GLT system is in service at one, initial

installation. This is a surface running application and the vehicles are manually driven.

AEG - M-Bahn

48.   The M-Bahn system has been under development for 13 years.   The first vehicle was   built   in   1975 and a construction of a test facility at   Braunschweig was begun in 1975. A contract was awarded in 1982 to build the system in Berlin which is planned to open for public service early in 1989. In 1985 the City of Las Vegas decided to adopt the system, and construction work began in 1988 with a planned opening date of 1991.   In 1988 a decision was made to select the M-Bahn system to link a new terminal with the existing one at Frankfurt Main Airport. The system uses electrically propelled magnetically levitated driverless vehicles running on segregated guideways are controlled from a central facility.   The vehicles are 12m long and 2.5m wide.   2 externally sliding doors each 1.3 m wide are provided on each side of the vehicles.   28 seats are provided with room for 64 standing   passengers   at $5/m^2$.   Wheel   chairs   can be accommodated. The vehicle is magnetically levitated. Each vehicle has two bogies carrying permanent magnets which support most of the weight by attraction upwards to steel support rails, one on either side of the guideway. Part (about 10%) of the vehicle's weight is always carried by small wheels and a mechanical linkage adjusts the gap between the magnets and the rails to compensate for varying loads. Small horizontal wheels running against vertical faces on the guideway provide lateral guidance.

49.   The guideway consists of longitudinal beams forming a trough in which the vehicles run and which also acts as an emergency walkway for passengers. The steel support rails, which are combined with the stator of the linear motor, and also provide the horizontal and vertical running surfaces for the guidance wheels, are attached to the inside of the trough. The guideway may be formed from steel or concrete as appropriate.   To date steel has been used for elevated guideways and concrete for those at grade.

50.   The M-Bahn system is an integrated system developed over a long period of time but which has not yet achieved public passenger carrying service, although it has received orders for further installations.

GEC - Automatic Light Rail System

51.   The GEC Automatic Light Rail System (ALRS) system was developed for the Docklands Light Railway in London.   It entered service in 1987, and this railway is now being extended and up-graded to meet increased demands. The system

uses basically conventional light rail vehicles with rotary traction motors. Current is collected from a low level conductor rail at 750V dc. An automatic control system has been developed, although the Train Captain who travels on every train is responsible for closing doors and initiating the start. The single articulated vehicle is 29 m long and 2.65 m wide with four bi-parting doors 1.4 m wide on each side which are used for normal and emergency access and egress. It provides for 84 seats and room for up to 176 standing passengers, each occupying $0.2m^2$. The body is of light welded steel construction with integration of main equipment cases, cable ducts, and air ducting into the main structural elements. Large windows, fluorescent lighting, and insulated walls contribute to passenger comfort.

52. Vehicles run on conventional railway track of 1435 mm gauge. Both ballasted or non-ballasted is used. Conventional railway turnouts are used.

53. The GEC ALRS uses well proven LRT vehicle technology which has been combined with an automatic control system developed for the Docklands Light Railway.

Von Roll Monorail Type III
54. The Von Roll Monorail Type III is in public passenger carrying service at Darling Harbour in Sydney, Australia. The system uses automatic rubber tyred, multiple articulated vehicles propelled by conventional rotary traction motors, which run straddling a central monorail beam. The articulated vehicle is 46 m long and 2.055 m wide. It comprises 10 individual units per vehicle. Each unit has one door 1.05 m wide on each side which are used for normal access and egress. Each unit provides for 8 seats and room for up to 9 standing passengers, each occupying $0.2m^2$. The total capacity per vehicle is 170 passengers. The body is of light construction and large windows, fluorescent lighting, and insulated walls contribute to passenger comfort.

55. Vehicles run on a monorail beam which is 940mm wide and 827mm high. Two types of switch have been developed, together with a traverser.

56. The Von Roll Monorail Type III is a proven system in passenger service. However it suffers from the disadvantage that vehicles cannot be coupled into trains to provide greater line capacities. Its present maximum line capacity is only 8500 passengers per hour per direction. The proposed Type IV Monorail is claimed to have a line capacity of 20000 passengers per hour per direction. However, design of this has not yet begun.

SUMMARY
   57.   A range of alternative systems have been described
in this paper. The choice between depends upon each
individual installation.   Generally it has been found that
those systems designed specifically for automatic operation
have the higher capital costs but can offer lower operating
costs. Typically, in a previous study of a network, capital
costs were found to range from £50M to £105M while annual
direct operating costs ranged from £1.6M to £2.3M at the same
level of demand. However there are wider considerations
relating to the public's perception of the different types of
system which strongly influence the final choice.

9. Moving people within urban centres

S. KEYS, BSC, MICE, MIHT, DipAF, MBIM, Winston Churchill Fellow in Rapid Transit Systems, Chief Assistant to Chief Executive, Project Manager of Southampton Rapid Transit Initiative, Southampton City Council

SYNOPSIS.   The paper describes the potential role of Light Transit Systems in moving people within urban centres.   Brief reviews are provided of principles of route selection, technical capabilities, customer requirements, environmental factors including potential for easing car parking and congestion, capital and operating costs.   Common features of existing working urban systems from around the World are discussed to provide the reader with basic scale information.

POTENTIAL ROLE OF LIGHT TRANSIT SYSTEMS IN URBAN CENTRES

1. The growth of property investment over the last decade has or is about to produce a spatial expansion of facilities.   This is especially so in redeveloping urban centres which have mature areas for residence, retail, business, industry, leisure, culture and heritage.   For urban centres to work effectively the spatial balance between established areas, new areas of development and the fixed transport terminals of airport, railway station, ferry, car parks, bus and coach stations needs to be maintained.   Spatial balance is a function of two things -

> (i) the uniqueness of the facility
> (ii) the quality of access to it.

As a simple example, the same person who invests considerable energy in visiting a major international sporting event will often baulk at walking several hundred metres to make a routine purchase like a sandwich.   For urban centres to ultimately succeed as providers of facilities the quality of access to and between component buildings must be of a sufficient standard to produce a contemporary spatial balance.

2. Historically the central urban resident and visitor, the 'customer', has completed the final leg of their journey on foot from their home or one of the transport terminii. This has not been too great a hardship when the distance is less than 500 metres, when the weather is favourable and when the person is fit and active. However, the customer becomes progressively disinclined to make journeys when the required walk distance is over 1000 metres, the weather is unfavourable and the customer is not fit and active. In such circumstances the spatial balance needs of the customer require either that the distance between origin and destination is shortened or a quality form of transport is available. Since it is often impractical to move major transport terminii closer together or to new developments, the solution is to implement an appropriate light transit system. Such a system would ideally link existing transport terminals together and with both existing and new development. Failure to implement such a system will result in additional car-bourne movement/congestion/pollution/frustration and ultimately make the centre a less attractive place to visit.

3. In making transit journeys in the 1 to 5 kilometre range customers demand high service levels of operation.

Typically these include:

combinations of short wait times and rapid progression times so that overall journey times are substantially quicker than walking or driving;

easy vehicular access for all including the disabled, the shopper with a trolley, or the parent with a pushchair;

fares that are modest and easy to collect;

all weather capability with reliability and safety;

a comfortable ride quality.

Existing transport providers will support a Light Transit System (LTS) implementation if:

the LTS service complements without disrupting their provision ie it does not interfere with the highway, the railway, the airport or the ferry operation.

Turning these aspirations into a broad performance specification has two main interelated themes:

(i) the selection of an appropriate route
(ii) the selection of an appropriate technology.

4.   To be successful, system routes must take account of the main people movements, both now and in the future, and existing radial transport movements.   The main car parks should be linked together and with the main public transport terminals and with the main urban residential, retail, business, industry, leisure, culture and heritage areas.   Emphasis should be made on selecting a route that will be accepted by a majority of citizens, interest groups, political groups and commercial interests.   The route should maximise system operating revenue opportunities by integrating to the fullest extent with existing and proposed facilities.   Acceptability of a given system route will depend on the technology chosen. The interface between route and technology is flexibility, particularly flexibility to easily extend initial routes.

5.   Prime technology requirements are to deliver a convenient, comfortable, cost-effective, safe, reliable, environmentally acceptable service.   All suitable current technologies deploy frequent electrically powered vehicles running over, on, or under a dedicated track.   The most versatile systems offer the choice of operating underground, on the ground, or elevated, with grade negotiating abilities of 10% or better, turning radius of 20 metres or better and operation down to 1 minute headway.

Such frequent operation naturally leads to vehicles having fully automatic command control and protection systems, obviating the need for drivers. Automated ticketing also allows unstaffed stations.   A uniformed presence is usually deployed around the system to assist the public and protect revenue. The whole operation is monitored by a central control centre that has visual and audio links with stations and vehicles.   Level floor boarding at stations, good quality seating/standing space, heating, ventilation and information signing, provide the user with a convenient, comfortable journey.

When operated without a driver the system must utilise a segregated or exclusive track. Such exclusive track can be at grade with suitable fencing but is most commonly found elevated or in tunnel. Utilising an exclusive track brings a further major benefit to transport in an urban centre. Users' desire for short overall journey times can be met without interruption of established transport activity.

6.   Capacity of such systems are between 600 and 15000 passengers per hour in each track direction. Such capacity is obtained by frequent operation of vehicles having individual carrying capacities of between 20 and 150 passengers in mixed seating/standing configurations. Individual vehicles can be automatically coupled together throughout the day to match surveyed patronage demand/time profiles.

7.   Station platforms are the limiting factor to system patronage growth. Whether platforms are underground, at grade or elevated, their length should be accurately determined. Increasing platform length is a very expensive and disruptive experience relative to new build. In common with vehicles, platform density will probably be 0.2 to 0.25 square metres per person. Further, given that the most common internal width for new vehicles is about 2.3 metres, the headway and the required capacity are known, then the arithmetic to deduce platform length is straightforward.

8.   Stations which are either underground or elevated will require special design to fit into the urban scene. They will require additional facilities of suitable lifts to provide access from pavement level to platform level to fully meet the needs of the disabled.

ENVIRONMENTAL CONSIDERATIONS

9. Electric tracked transport systems have a high energy efficiency even allowing for the energy required for initial construction as can be seen in Table 1.

TABLE 1

Comparisons of Energy required to move 220,000 urban passenger miles per day
(MKWH = Millions of Kilowatt Hours)

	PER YEAR MKWH
a) People Mover	
Construction 30 MKWH over 30 year life (fully elevated track)	1
Operation of Vehicles	1.4
Operation of Stations	1.2
Operation of Remainder	0.4
Energy Total a)	4.0
b) Minibus at 20 passengers per bus	
Fossil fuel consumed 0.56 million gallons/year	
Energy Total b)	7.7
c) Private car at 2 passengers per car	
Fossil fuel consumed 1.58 million gallons/year	
Energy Total	21.5

Comparison.
People Mover energy consumed = 52% Minibus Equivalent
= 19% Private Car Equivalent

Table 1 Comparison of Energy requirements to move 220,000 urban passenger miles per day.

10. Air pollution is of great concern. Table 2 describes the air pollution associated with 100,000 fossil fuel urban vehicles miles per day expressed over a full year.

Table 2

Constituent Pollutants caused by burning fossil fuel to undertake 100,000 urban vehicle miles per day		
		Tonnes per Year
Greenhouse	Carbon Dioxide	16,200
	Carbon Monoxide	2,520
Acid Rain	Hydro Carbons	216
	Nitrogen Oxide	144
	Lead	1

Table 2. Air Pollution associated with 100,000 fossil fuel urban vehicle miles per day expressed over a full year.

People Movers are non-polluting in operation. But equally important is the spatial balance effect (para 1), the strengthening of public transport integration and the reduction in unnecessary cross centre traffic movements (para 16).

A good people mover introduction will greatly assist in reducing air pollution in an urban centre.

11. The public often voices apprehension over potential noise and vibration when an urban people mover is proposed. It is therefore worth comparing common transport generated noise levels, Table 3.

Table 3

Source	dBA at 7.5 Metres from source
People Mover	65
Motor car	71
Bus	81
Lorry	82
Railway Train	85+

Table 3. Comparison of typical noise levels generated by various transport modes.

A noise generation of 65dBA is the equivalent of the noise level in a modern office or a busy restaurant. Looking at the comparison another way, a typical people mover system would generate less than a quarter of the noise generated by a railway train, less than half the noise of a bus and would be quieter than a motor car. In order to obtain quality of ride, track beams must present an even continuous surface, leading to extremely low levels of vibration.

12.   The satisfactory working of an urban centre during construction of a people mover will be of concern to all sectors of the community. Traditional in situ techniques requiring substantial false-work for an extended period will be unacceptable for many urban situations. It is therefore essential that substantial elements of the works are prefabricated and erected at times designed to minimise urban disruption. A typical construction sequence might be bore pile and cap foundation, transport to site and erect precast columns (spacing 20 to 40 metres), transport to site and erect precast track beams, complete stations and depot using conventional building techniques, complete electrical and communication work, transport vehicles to completed trackway, install ticketing systems, test, tune vehicle suspension to trackway, set computer timings, retest and open to public. The construction period would of course depend on the ratio of stations to track but assuming a typical frequency of a station every 500 metres one would expect total construction time to be 3 to 8 months per double elevated track kilometre depending on project scale.

13.   Concern is often expressed that an elevated people mover cannot visually sit comfortably within an established urban scene. This will always be a matter for subjective judgment and will, of course, depend as much on route selection as quality of design and execution. The structures are especially suited to large open areas where they can add a sense of excitement. Photographs 1, 2 and 3 illustrate the possibilities. New development can be built around track with the station platform wholly within a building (low floor loadings, low noise levels, little vibration). In such circumstances the concept of a "horizontal passenger lift" is fully realised.

Photograph 1
Traditionally constructed Terminus Station

Photograph 2
Partial integration at a new development

Photograph 3
Track crossing over a highway

Photographs courtesy of Southampton City Council and Briway Transit Systems, Cranleigh, Surrey.

GENERALISED COSTS AND BENEFITS

14.   Capital costs for exclusive elevated double track people movers vary considerably depending on capacity requirements, number of stations and size of system.   A cost profile for new build systems excluding land is provided in Table 4.

Table 4

ELEMENT	PERCENTAGE OF COST
Guideway (rights of way preparation and construction of elevated track)	35
Stations	15
Depot	2
Signalling/Control	8
Generating/Converting Plant	4
Cables and feeders	4
Vehicles	22
Other (Design, project management minor structures, testing)	10
	100

Table 4. Possible Cost Profile for an elevated urban People Mover.

A 'budget' cost per double track kilometre might be in the range £7 million to £18 million based on fully elevated track. Tunnelling would increase costs whilst surface running would depress costs.

15. Operational costs vary with the size of required system. Unit operational costs per passenger kilometre fall as the route system gets larger and core costs become distributed over a wider base. The annual operating budget of say a 10Km double elevated track system might be in the range £1.5 million to £3.5 million depending on capacity requirements.

16.   Many benefits flow from connecting the key components of an urban centre.

Socially.   Central   area facilities become more accessible and people are better able to enjoy more of the varied attractions that make urban centres unique.   Better use promotes better quality which promotes better use.   A positive cycle to make urban centres more socially user-friendly.

Economically. Promoting better circulation results in a general strengthening of local trade, the local economy and the ability to attract and retain good employers.

Commercially. Increased customer flow results in increased value per unit area of floor space.   This "added value" is generally on a graduating scale, being high in the immediate vicinity of station loca tions to neutral at a radius of 500 metres.

"Planning gain" can result by allowing individual sites to develop with more density and fulfill car parking obligations on more remote, less valuable land.

Transport. Linking the key transport modes together encourages greater use of public transport as over- all attraction is enhanced.   It becomes convenient to a larger sector of the community to use public transport if joint use ticketing arrangements result in customers obtaining quicker, cheaper and better access to final destinations.

Linking the major car parks together, installing an intelligent information signing, monitoring system and linking with major attractions can produce very positive benefits.   By directing motorists to available car spaces nearest their point of arrival in the centre rather than allowing them to randomly search for spaces nearest their destination can produce significant benefits - reduction in conges- tion, air pollution, noise and frustration!

COMMON FEATURES FOUND IN WORKING LIGHT TRANSIT SYSTEMS SERVING URBAN CENTRES

17.   In discussing common features found in people movers I acknowledge that there are always exceptions and should I fail, therefore, to mention a unique feature of a particular system I apologise to that manufacturer.

18.   Single track width varies between 1 metre and 4.5 metres depending on the form of associated emergency walkway. Track geometry can vary to suit client requirements both vertically and horizontally. Gradients should not exceed 10% although some systems will tolerate 12.5%. The majority of systems will negotiate radii of 30 metres with progressively fewer able to negotiate smaller radii down to 6 metres. Supports to elevated track are generally at 20 to 40 metre centres. Construction material can be steel but is usually reinforced concrete.

19.   Vehicles are usually powered by direct current electricity although alternating current is very occasionally used. Most systems have standby battery power for use in an emergency. Technologies include magnetic levitation, hover air cable hauled, linear motor with steel wheels on steel rails for guidance and driven inflated rubber tyred wheels. The latter is the most common. Individual external vehicle size will typically be of the order 10m long x 2.5m wide x 3.6m high. All standing capacity can be approximately deduced by multiplying the gross internal floor area (measured in square metres) by five. The average progression speed of the vehicle in an urban centre with frequent stations will be 25 to 40 kilometres per hour depending on track alignment. Maximum speed is usually governed to be 80 to 100 kilometres per hour. As a comparison, a progression speed of 15 to 20 kilometres per hour is a guide to average door to door urban car journeys (including access) for journeys below 5 kilometres in length. A typical urban pedestrian progression speed would be 5 kilometres per hour. Common features found in vehicles include either full air conditioning or efficient heating/ ventilation system, sealed windows, high lighting standards (emergency lighting), passenger emergency call button, two-way voice communication system, public address system, level vehicle/station platform floors, route maps, seating, standing with grab rails. Vehicles are driverless due to automatic signalling and control systems.

20.   Signalling and control systems usually employ sophisticated vehicle detection and vehicle protection systems which govern the minimum distance between vehicles and station dwell times.   Information is relayed to a control centre.

21.   A control centre(s) provides total surveillance and control of the system.   Typical display within   the   control   room   would   include   mimic diagrams, visual display units, TV screens and video recording equipment.   Vehicle dispatch and regulation is automatic but can, under appropriate procedures, be manually overriden by central control.

22.   A private telephone network usually links the   stations,   the   control   centre,   the   depot, electricity sub-stations and maintenance workshops. The two-way communication system in the vehicles and at   stations   links them with   control   centre.   A dedicated telephone link is normally provided to all emergency services.

23.   Stations   provide basic facilities: canopies,   automatic   ticket   vending   machines,   seats, route   maps,   lighting,   station   signage,   rubbish disposal units, non-slip surfaces, attractive easy to   clean and visually pleasant surface treatments, and   not-so-basic   facilities: video   surveillance cameras,   public   address and two-way communication system with central control, zoned fire detection system,   central   monitoring   of   all   equipment. Access   to platforms is by a combination   of lifts, escalators, stairways and ramps.

24.   Platforms (para 7) are typically 20 to   50 metres   long.   Width   depends on capacity   but   an island   platform   would typically be 4 metres   to   8 metres.   Platform height above track is typically 1 metre.   Platform   doors   are   sometimes   used, especially when a station is wholly located within a host building.

25.   The depot is usually, though not   necessarily,   located   adjacent   to the route and is   often combined with the control centre.   Depot functions include   visual inspections of vehicles and   track, acting on vehicle diagnostic printouts, cleaning and washing of vehicles, component removal repair and overhaul,   repairs to mechanical,   electrical, electronic and trim,   wheel balancing and tyre changing, vehicle   spraying.   The   size   of the depot   will depend on   the   size of the vehicle fleet but is likely to be in the region of 2,000 to 5,000 square

metres. All the accommodation does not have to be on one level. A multistorey building might combine depot, station, control centre, car parking and commercial uses to maximise land use.

26. The control of system vandalism is a proper concern. Vandalism at stations is not of the same magnitude as public transport stations generally, simply because of the very short wait times between vehicles and the fact that stations are normally secured when not in use. Video surveillance/recording, a public address system and direct links to the Police provide proven deterrents to vandalism. Passengers within a sealed vehicle are "captive" so egress is impossible if central control overrides automatic operation and holds culprits until Police arrive.

27. Reliability of people movers is very high - better than 99.8% measured against exacting performance criteria. Safety standards are particularly impressive with operational accidents being exceptionally low.

28. Should a vehicle fail in passenger service three options are usually available -

i) the vehicle might continue on auxilliary battery power to the next station;

ii) another vehicle might automatically couple to the failed vehicle, recovering it first to the nearest station and then to the depot;

iii) passengers are advised via the public address system to leave the vehicle, using the emergency doors and walkway to access the nearest station.

29. The length of the operating day is typically 15 to 18 hours with a peak service frequency of a vehicle every 120 seconds. A significant uniformed presence is provided throughout the route to both assist the public and protect revenue.

SUMMARY

30. With the right choice of route and technology an exclusive track electrically powered high frequency transit system does have a place for distributing people around city centres. When such systems also integrate with established transport terminals the social, environmental, economic,

commercial and transport benefits can be significant. Provided mechanisms can be found to fund
such initiatives a higher percentage of UK urban
centres wishing to utilise such technology will
succeed in obtaining a convenient, comfortable,
cost-effective way of moving people without disruption to established transport activity.

Discussion on papers 8 and 9

A. COOKSEY, Department of Transport Railway Inspectorate
Much as been said about the choice and different types of
system available but also of selling the LRT system to a
number of different bodies: Government, developers, local
authorities and, very importantly, to the public. However, we
all must take care to be clear about what we are selling, and
we must be honest as to what we are selling, especially to the
public. The price of misrepresenting the product could be
extremely high. Some will know that in Hong Kong I walked
into an enormous problem because the majority of the public,
and even some of the involved Government Departments, did not
appreciate the Tuen Mun LRT system was a modern tramway and
not a mass transit railway. I am the first member of the
Inspectorate to have an accident inquiry report published in
Chinese and to have to conduct the investigation and system
inspection with a police escort.

It is important that the selling is done but it is perhaps
even more important for safety reasons to start educating the
public, and especially other road users, as early as possible.
However safe the LRT system its level of safety is very much
dependent on others. Getting the safety equation wrong will
not only damage your system but everyone else's schemes as
well.

R. A. MCKITTRICK, Scott Wilson Kirkpatrick
Having been involved with Scott Wilson Kirkpatrick for seven
years in Hong Kong on the Tuen Mun LRT I must respond to Mr
Cooksey's comments.

To understand the situation fully you must live and work in
the Far East. One of my staff once said to me, in relation to
accidents, that 'life in Hong Kong is cheap'. In other words
people take more risks than in western society. The
electrification of the Kowloon–Canton Railway resulted in
several deaths as, prior to electrification, villagers used

the railway reserve as a footway and, in spite of a massive publicity campaign, continued to do so afterwards.

The Tuen Mun system was explained and 'sold' to the public well in advance. There were, I think, no more than two or three deaths. In its first year of operation the system had 14 accidents involving pedestrians compared with 6000 vehicle/pedestrian accidents in Hong Kong in the same period.

It worries me, and my colleagues in Hong Kong, that the wrong impression should be gained of the Tuen Mun LRT. Contrary to hearsay it is an excellent example of contemporary LRT practice. We must not allow a few accidents to hinder the development in the UK of some potentially super schemes which will contain lengths of shared street running.

G. HOWARD, Paper 8

I agree that it is important to ensure that the public are fully aware of the effects of introducing a new LRT system, and the safety implications are fully explored. The Tuen Mun system, to which reference was made, did experience a number of incidents during the initial period of operation, several of which could be ascribed to the public's unawareness of the nature of the system. (However one or two could, I believe, be ascribed to human error on the part of staff). The result was considerable adverse publicity in the local media, although I am told that the old tramway system on Hong Kong Island experiences more frequent incidents which are not generally reported in the media. Recent discussions on the safety of air transport have led to the argument that the present acceptable accident rate would become unacceptable to the public as the number of reported accidents increase as a result in the growth of air traffic.

It is interesting to note that a number of concerns raised about the introduction of LRT are often alleviated following visits to existing continental systems and seeing them in operation.

D. S. HELLEWELL, Greater Manchester Metrolink

In my experience it is possible, by skilful design, to combine a line-haul and central area distribution system. If there is a separate central area/downtown distributor one introduces an additional interchange in what is often a short journey. How does one overcome this problem?

New systems have to cater for those people with mobility impairments. How does one achieve this cost-effectively with the elevated systems?

G. HOWARD, Paper 8

Experience shows that having to change from one line or mode to another is unpopular with passengers. The perceived penalty is, in terms of generalized time, considerably greater than the actual time involved. The best that can be hoped for, if interchange cannot be avoided, is to arrange a cross-platform interchange which, ideally, should apply to both directions of travel. The arrangements on the Hong Kong Mass Transit Railway are good examples of the way in which the interchange penalty can be minimized, although the solution involves extra expense.

It is expensive to cater for those people with a mobility handicap on any system which does not run at ground level. Lifts are necessary at elevated and underground stations to cater for the more severely mobility handicapped. Even those people with lesser handicaps may find it difficult to negotiate ramps, stairs, and escalators and, as a consequence of such 'user-unfriendliness' be deterred from making full use of the system.

S. KEYS, Paper 9

The service requirements of a line-haul and central area distributor system are, of course, different. A line-haul system carries volume by employing large vehicles, whereas a good distributor system carries volume by employing very frequent vehicles. Where there is justification of the two supporting each other, i.e. large vehicles at very frequent intervals, I would support Mr Hellewell. However, this criterion will only be met in very dense metropolitan areas not found in many British provincial cities of the 1990s. One may therefore have to use skilful design to make the interchange as convenient as possible. This will involve very short wait times, e.g. an average of 1 minute, direct convenient communication between rail, ferry, coach, bus, car, cycle and the distribution system. Once on the vehicle, rapid progression speeds will make even short journeys attractive.

New transit systems do indeed have to cater fully for people with mobility impairments. Given that central area stations will often be in host buildings with such facilities I can see no technical or financial problems in providing high quality access.

T. D. HAMILTON, <u>Durham County Council</u>

In response to the suggestion that alternative arrangements should be made for the disabled, there are six million people in the UK with a mobility handicap that makes it difficult or impossible to use public transport. For many, very simple improvements would allow them to use buses, trains, trams or metros.

The Department of Transport's DPTAC work shows the need and this been taken into account in many new buses and on the new generation of rapid transit systems planned for the UK. Street running not only makes life easier for the mobility handicapped, it is often safer for other groups who are PRT users.

The Tyne & Wear Metro, Paris RER and Metro, and Lyon and Marseilles Metros, for example, all require policing to combat mugging. In Marseilles the Metro is policed by men with alsatians!

S. KEYS, <u>Paper 9</u>

Certainly the public are entitled to expect their journeys to be protected from mugging and physical abuse. Mr Hamilton implies that automated and semi-automated systems are intrinsically deficient in this respect - a view I cannot share. Given visual and audio communication between vehicles, central control and both the systems uniformed staff and the police, there is a contrary view that personal physical safety can be very high on automated driverless systems.

DR L. LESLEY, <u>Liverpool Polytechnic</u>

Access for the mobility impaired will not only help the six million who are physically mobility impaired, but also adults whose mobility is impaired by being accompanied by children.

These new systems have at least half the costs of civil and track systems. New installations will be street running which, with existing track systems, requires considerable excavation and reinstatement of the highway. The new street track system announced in Bristol promises to cost about one-third of existing systems and will be demonstrated this year in Blackpool as a result of co-operation between BSC, Edgar Allan, James Walker and myself.

G. HOWARD, <u>Paper 8</u>

I do not believe that the suggestion that alternative arrangements should be made for people with a mobility handicap is acceptable or even practicable. As Mr Hamilton

pointed out, there are six million people in the UK with a
mobility handicap which makes it difficult for them to use
public transport. The UITP International Light Rail
Commission prepared a document on provision for the
handicapped which included the following definition.

> For public transport purposes the term `handicapped' or
> `disabled' includes all persons whose mobility is
> restricted by reasons of age, by temporary or permanent
> physical and/or sensory disability. It includes the
> elderly and the very young; those with slight or severe
> disabilities, affecting movement or grip of hands; hidden
> disabilities such as heart condition; the blind or
> partially sighted; the deaf or hard of hearing;
> epileptics; mentally handicapped, or those with recurring
> disabilities, and pregnant women. It also includes those
> who are `self-handicapped' with shopping, luggage, or
> children, with or without pushchairs. Depending on the
> statistical methods adopted in different countries, recent
> studies suggest that about 10% of a country's population
> may be considered as `transport disabled' or `mobility
> handicapped'.

In view of the numbers involved, it is difficult to see how
an effective alternative system could be provided. The object
must be to ensure that any new systems are made accessible to
as many of the population as possible. This should, as
suggested, ensure that the system becomes more user-friendly
and acceptable to the public at large.

10. Promotion and public consultation

R. F. DIXON, BEng, MICE, MCIT, Principal Transportation Planner, Metro Development Department, West Midlands Passenger Transport Executive

SYNOPSIS

Light rail is at a fragile stage in the United Kingdom. There are no "state of the art" examples at present. Technical excellence and cast-iron financial justification are of no value without public acceptance. Experience is being assessed in what the public want to know, what they ought to be told and the approaches to be used. During the last five years the West Midlands has arguably produced the greatest strength of public feeling against light rail proposals. A comprehensive understanding is being gained of how public support is lost and how to try to win it back.

INTRODUCTION

1. The definition of "promote" is "to initiate or help forward the process or formation of", which contains no surprises. The definition of (public) consultation is "to seek information or advice from (the public)", but is that really what we think we are doing in public consultation exercises or indeed is it what we should be doing?

2. In 1985 the West Midlands County Council resolved that the Passenger Transport Executive should promote a Bill for a light rail line in Birmingham. The line was designed in a remarkably short period of time, or with indecent haste, depending upon your point of view. Public consultation was scheduled to start a few days after the official presentation to Birmingham City Council.

3. The scheme was technically sound and was either in tunnel or totally segregated from highway traffic except at highway crossings. Highway junctions which were affected were redesigned to accommodate the additional light rail traffic signal phase while at the same time preserving highway capacity. The price of the technical excellence was the need to demolish up to 238 houses.

4. The public consultation exercise began, "seeking advice and information from the public". Although the information received was a little lacking, the advice arrived freely and in large quantities and ranged from the spirited through the fatally injurious to the obscene. The Bill was not deposited in 1985 but what had gone wrong.

5. In short, one or more vital stages had been omitted due to the shortened timescale. It is pointless "seeking advice and information" from the public when they have not the faintest conception of the subject about which their advice and information is being sought. It is also pointless seeking advice and information from the public if that is not really what you want. The level of advice and information which can be forthcoming on a fait accompli is limited.

6. The two stages omitted in 1985 were Education, general information about light rail, and Options, true public consultation about the available alternatives.

EDUCATION

7. The very first phase of promotion is education. With many products this is not necessary as the majority know what is meant by soap powder, dog food or lager. With light rail, education is vital as very few people know what it is. If it is described as an improved form of public transport many people would not be impressed. Their current perception of public transport is so bad (banana buses, late trains) that "improved" means merely "less poor". This is especially true in the non public transport user sector, a major target market for light rail systems. So, how do we begin to get across an accurate image of the product we are trying to "sell" - light rail. A definition could be a good start but is not as easy to provide as it may seem. If I summarise the definition in the P.T.E. Group's "Light Rail Transit" report (ref.1) then light rail is: "a system of manually driven vehicles which run by means of steel wheels on steel rails, are capable of negotiating tighter curves and steeper gradients than conventional rail vehicles and are wholly or partially segregated or unsegregated from road traffic". This is not easily memorable or comprehensible and what mental image will it conjure? Light rail can be defined as "a modern tram system" which if nothing else is truthful but to those who remember British trams, can be almost totally misleading. In other words, definitions are unlikely to assist the public's perception of light rail.

8. What is required is an image and the image begins with a brand name. How many products which require promotion or marketing do not have brand names? Very few, and a light rail scheme should be the same. Since September 1987, light rail in the West Midlands has been "Midland Metro". In Manchester it is "Metrolink", in West Yorkshire

"Metrorider" and in South Yorkshire "Supertram". The name should be fairly short, memorable and vaguely relevant. Otherwise anything goes, although I would not expect the marketing men to agree.

9. With the name there must be a visual image or in other words a logo, a style and a colour scheme which together form the corporate identity. To many in the civil engineering profession, the tacky hype appears pretentious and unnecessary. On the contrary, until the public are aware of what light rail transit really is, it is essential.

10. Now that the product exists the education process can begin.

11. The major media launch of the brand name can be very effective if it is done correctly. It must be remembered that the media are not necessarily interested in the product but they are interested in getting a story and so a few, and only a few, facts should be produced which are memorable, comprehensible and most of all immensely impressive. These will form the basis for the headline and the first paragraph of the story. The fill will come from the press release. If enough interest can be generated at the launch then subsequent approaches to the local papers should secure the occasional feature article about your system which keeps it in the public eye and reaches a very large audience for virtually no outlay. The media (press, regional television and local radio) play a vital role in the education process and must be kept aware of developments at all times.

12. The leaflet which accompanies the launch and subsequent leaflets with supplementary information should follow the same basic rules. They should be short, never longer than A3 folded in half to give four A4 sides; they should be colourful and attractive with the logo and brand name prominently displayed; they should be of sufficiently high quality to make people want to have one, after all it may be all they have to remember you by, but not of such high quality that everyone especially the children will want ten each; and, most of all, it must inform. It should therefore contain attractive unedited photographs of similar systems elsewhere which should be well presented as they form the first introduction to light rail for the majority of your audience. In addition there should be additional information of a general nature about why it is needed, its size, speed, noise emission, lack of pollutant emission, power supply and frequency.

13. The leaflet forms the basis of the initial education process and is therefore the framework for the preparation of what has become the almost obligatory video or videos. A longer more detailed presentation, but no more than 10 minutes, is appropriate for politicians and opinion formers, but a shorter presentation of 5 - 6 minutes can contain all that the public will want to see at their first

sitting. Videos are generally well received but beware of the sceptics. We have been accused of "removing all the overhead gantries" from some footage of the Grenoble system. The dear lady would just not believe that there were no gantries there in the first place.

14. Armed with the leaflets and the video the next phase is to sell the message to as many professional, trade and public organisations as possible. Presentations to large groups are productive at this stage and should be given at every opportunity. Do not wait to be asked. Target those local organisations which need to know about your proposed system and invite yourself along by offering to give a presentation to a meeting in the near future. The Programme Secretary is usually desperately short of speakers and will welcome you with open arms. Prime targets are Chambers of Commerce and Trade, Central Area Traders Associations, professional institutions, employers' groups, major employers' social society meetings, local general interest groups, transport enthusiasts' organisations and schools. A .certain amount of care must be taken with the last category if the available manpower is not to be tied up for the foreseeable future but it must be remembered that children are the most receptive to an education programme and they are your future customers.

15. The public in general are more difficult to track down and Midland Metro uses a converted single deck bus as a mobile meeting room/exhibition area/video viewing room. The bus has been used extensively to visit shopping centres, libraries, shows and other weekend events to spread the Metro message as widely as possible.

16. Midland Metro has also used give-aways on a limited scale, mainly hats and badges, and has sponsored a small number of events. The constant aim is to maintain a high level of public awareness to Midland Metro, what it stands for and what it aims to do in the overall sense.

17. It is absolutely essential to avoid any discussion on alignments, routes or even corridors at this stage. The only route information given during the education phase was that shown in Figure 1. This policy is strictly adhered to in all areas where options have not been developed. This avoids unnecessary blight and unwarranted public concern as well as minimising the number of potential objectors to be faced at any time.

18. Throughout the above process it is essential that the Members and Chief Officers of the appropriate District Councils are kept one step ahead in the education process. Following the problems in 1985 when there was little if any communication through official channels between West Midlands County Council and Birmingham City Council, the Passenger Transport Authority and Executive have recognised the benefits to be gained from a joint approach with the Districts. It is vitally important that representatives of

DIXON

the politicians in the Districts, some of whom sit on the Passenger Transport Authority, are fully briefed about light rail including visits to systems such as Hanover, Nantes or Grenoble if possible. Once the District politicians have agreed in principle to the development of Midland Metro in their Borough that is the time for detailed discussions with their officers to begin.

19. The Districts will ask the same questions and will have the same goals as the general public but on a more global scale, for instance:
- In general terms, what is in it for them?
- Will the Districts have to make a contribution to the capital cost?
- How will Midland Metro affect planning policies?
- Will the prospects of the economy and the redevelopment of the area be improved?
- What are the effects on residential, commercial and industrial property?
- Will the environment be affected for better or worse?
- Will there be affects on the highway network?

20. The involvement of virtually every District department emphasises the need for a tangible and coordinated approach to route finding and option selection.

21. Midland Metro now enjoys all-party support from the Members of the Passenger Transport Authority and political commitment from each of the seven District Councils.

22. It is never too early in the promotion process to begin briefing, and lobbying, local Members of Parliament. If one of their constituents should ask a question about the proposed system then the M.P. will expect to have at least some background information. The lobbying of M.E.P.'s, other Members of Parliament and Peers, especially those with transport interests, can take place a little later but is vitally important and must not be forgotten.

23. The education phase will continue until at least the opening of the first line at which time the reality will become the greatest educational asset.

OPTIONS

24. The first test of this commitment and support was the selection of Line 1 between Birmingham and Wolverhampton for submission as a Bill to Parliament in November 1988. The route was one of four corridors selected by the four Black Country District Councils for investigation as Midland Metro lines.

25. Line 1 was exceptional in several ways. There was only one short stretch (2km) over which options were available, the remainder (18km) being on a former rail alignment. Capital costs were low at £3m. per kilometre. Little property was required and there were few adverse affects on residential or industrial property. This was borne out by the relatively speedy and fairly painless

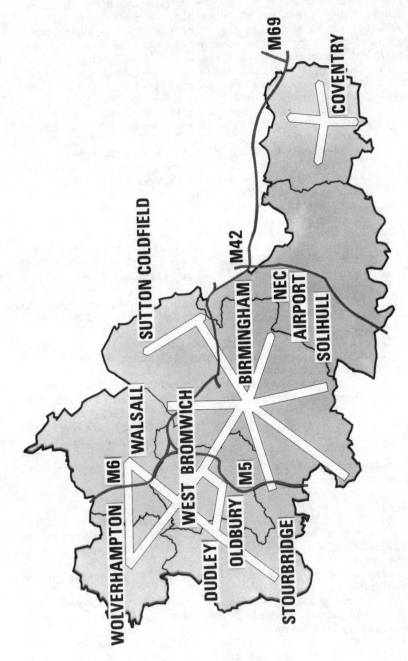

FIG. 1 The initial network of Midland Metro corridors.

settlement of the few petitions that were lodged against the Bill. Although the public consultation machine sprang into action there was little for it to do. The main public complaint was that they had so long to wait for it to open. Line 1 should have received Royal Assent in November, 1989.

26. Far more typical in terms of public consultation effort are Line 2 between Birmingham and the National Exhibition Centre and Birmingham International Airport and Line 3 between Wolverhampton, Walsall and Dudley, which were submitted as the Midland Metro No. 2 Bill in November 1989.

27. The former runs through three large residential areas, one on the outskirts of the City of Birmingham at Bromford and two in Chelmsley Wood in the Borough of Solihull. A series of options were developed along the route including tunnel and street-running options in Birmingham City Centre as well as segregated and street-running options in the large residential areas. Following an initial sieving of the available alternatives a total of 16 options were put forward for consultation along various parts of the route. Only 30% of the route was considered to be fixed at this stage.

28. The Wolverhampton-Walsall-Dudley route, Line 3, is based on former or existing rail lines with on-street or segregated sections making up the remainder. There was thus less scope for options but these were developed whenever the route left former rail alignments and the possibility existed.

29. The initial public consultation exercise for Lines 2 and 3 was phased between March and June 1989 beginning in Walsall and ending in Solihull. Long sections of both lines produced no adverse reaction and often positive support. The story was different in two of the three residential areas on Line 2, and in two residential areas on Line 3. There was no clear favourite between the tunnel or on-street options in Birmingham City Centre and this issue was resolved on engineering, planning and cost grounds which pointed to the shorter of the tunnel options. Following the initial series of visits by the exhibition bus to all the areas along lines 2 and 3, the public consultation exercise was concentrated in the residential areas where objections had been raised.

30. The public had a wide range of questions but for guidance here are some examples:
- Does it demolish my house?
- Does it go very near to my house?
- What is it?
- Where is it going?
- Why can't it go somewhere else? (NIMBY)
- Why can't it go anywhere else? (NIMBY-NOTE)
- What does it look like? (a high speed train, a diesel multiple unit, an old tram?)

- Will it have overhead gantries?
- How noisy will it be? (a high speed train etc?)
- Why do we need it?
- We don't need it, do we?
- How much will it cost the ratepayer to build?
- How much will the fares be?
- How much room will it take up?
- There isn't enough room to fit it in, is there? (whether there is or not).
- What happens if it breaks down?
- What happens if a bicycle tyre (or stiletto heel) gets stuck in the grooved tracks?
- What happens if a (wet/dry) kite string touches the overhead wires?
- What happens if a carbon fibre fishing rod touches the overhead wires?
- What voltage (or more technically, amperage) are the overhead lines?
- What affect will the overhead lines have on short-wave radio, pacemakers, television reception and lightning strikes?

31. Whilst not exhaustive the above attempts to represent the full range, from the defendable through the inevitable to the impossible. What the list does show is that no matter how good the education phase is, there will be many who have not been reached or who have not cared to listen. Only the prospect of being affected draws and concentrates their attention. The range of questions also emphasises the importance of input by technical staff during the public consultation phase. The PR people cannot do it on their own.

32. The initial responses for Line 2 revealed that Midland Metro had become involved with and rekindled a longstanding battle by the residents of one residential area for better environmental conditions. Along the edge of the area runs the elevated and very busy M6 motorway. Adjacent to that is a main railway line. Above them is the flight path to Birmingham International Airport as well as high voltage power cables.

33. Midland Metro will not affect noise levels but is seized upon as the ideal vehicle for airing residents' grievances. Whilst the logic behind the residents' actions is clear, such a situation does not provide the best scenario within which to explain Metro's benefits. The irony is that Metro is the only one of the perceived or real problems that actually provides any benefits to the residents at all.

34. Further along Line 2 a similar but possibly less severe problem arose. The villain of the piece was again the M6 motorway which in this case lurked behind a noise bund. Residents living near to the bund were naturally concerned that no part of it should be removed thus

worsening their environmental conditions.

35. In both of the above cases the presence of options helped to defuse the situation and permit a reasoned debate of the issues to take place. Even if the residents ultimately choose to take their objections to Parliament it will not be through any lack of exchange of ideas. It could have more to do with the fact that the residents' favourite option, not to build Metro at all, would not be entertained by the District Councils or the Passenger Transport Authority.

36. Elsewhere on Line 2 and at two sites on Line 3 no feasible options presented themselves. This tends to bring about a role reversal and it is the residents who start to design the scheme and to produce the options. If they come up with a good one it is usually a good idea to accept it, however grudgingly. Unfortunately this was not our experience.

THE RESIDENTS GROUP

37. All of the above situations had a common factor - the formation of a residents group. A well organised group can often appear to be an unwelcome thorn in the side but can also assist the education and consultation processes. The group committee can perform a valuable role by distributing information about Metro and collecting residents' views. Such an arrangement can work very well and positively contribute to the final form of the scheme. There can be problems however. Residents' groups have an overwhelming desire to organise public meetings. From the groups' point of view these can provide a morale-boosting show of support in the form of numbers, noise or both. From the promoters viewpoint they are likely to achieve little if anything and should be avoided at all costs. Unless the meeting is run by a Chairman with exceptional skills the event will deteriorate into an unstructured shouting match at which nobody's views are aired or discussed. Small group meetings with say 10 - 20 people can be far more productive.

38. A further problem with residents groups is that the transfer of information from engineer to committee member has to cross the professional/layman divide which can result in the unwitting, or even deliberate, corruption of data when passed from committee to resident. A similar affect works in reverse. No self respecting residents group is going to admit that it does not have the total support of at least 90% of the community whatever the reality of the situation might be. The way in which residents groups carry out surveys, and the results produced, cannot always be relied upon.

39. A good residents group will provide positive and stimulating opposition and will undoubtedly improve the quality of the scheme with their invaluable local knowledge and willingness to take part in an exchange of information.

A poor residents group will be totally negative, will clutch at straws and relentlessly pursue answers to questions which have been answered many times before. Such a group contributes nothing and usually, therefore, receives nothing from the consultation process.

PLANS

40. It is not unreasonable for members of the public to ask to see plans of the proposals about which they are being consulted. The type of plan to be provided requires careful consideration and I offer no recommendation. The options stage is the most difficult. Superimposing the options on a Geographia or A-Z street map base allows the majority of the public to easily orientate themselves and obtain a basic understanding of where the routes will go. This approach is criticised because of the lack of detail and the misunderstandings that the exaggerated street widths can bring about. A 1:10,000 OS base has no such distortion problems but still suffers from lack of detail. The alternative is to use 1:2500 or even 1:1250 OS base. The detail is now clear, so clear that the options have to be designed far more than is really necessary. This approach is criticised because the plans look to be so advanced that the public immediately suspects that work is about to start at any moment and so question the point of the consultation exercise.

POTENTIAL USERS

41. A body of people which could play a major role in the consultation process are the potential users of the system. Unfortunately these tend to be difficult to find. Few opponents of the system admit to a desire to use it and the majority tend to become instant experts at forecasting travel demand, predicting that usage in their area will be nil. It is always more difficult to rally supporters into vocal action than it is to find vociferous objectors. It is vitally important that the benefits of light rail are hammered home in terms of reliability, lower journey times, comfort and frequency so that the silent majority is aware of the positive aspects of the scheme as well as the real or imaginary disbenefits which are constantly being raised by the minority opposition groups. The size of this minority will be discussed in para 47.

BUSINESS INTEREST AND INDUSTRY CONSULTATION

42. In parallel with the consultation process for the public, the views of industrial and commercial interests must be sought along the route or routes. These discussions tend to be less emotional than those with the public and fewer questions need to be answered. The two basic pieces of information required by a business interest whose property is to be acquired are:

- Can the business be relocated?
- What will the compensation cover?

Less successful businesses omit the former question. When only part of a property is to be acquired, or access is to be affected, then the necessary accommodation works can be far more of a problem and should not be under-estimated. The balance between what needs to be done and what the owner has been intending to do for years can be difficult to strike. What the system is and where it goes are secondary issues. From businesses not physically affected but close to a proposed route the primary issues are whether the line will improve business and whether staff recruitment will be easier because access will have improved.

GROUPS AND ASSOCIATIONS

43. Finally but by no means least in terms of importance or difficulty are the consultations with interested groups and associations. These include organisations for the disabled, cyclists groups, motoring organisations and groups for the elderly, among others. These discussions conform with the definition of consultation discussed earlier in that there is a true exchange of views between the promoters, the potential users and those potentially affected. The benefits of light rail are more easily recognised and understood by these groups than by the public at large. This does not make it easier to meet the conflicting requirements and interests but reinforces the need for continuous contact during the design stages to achieve the nearest thing possible to consensus.

CONCLUSION

44. In the absence of widespread familiarity with light rail in this country, the prerequisite for a promotion and public participation exercise is a major education and marketing programme. This will be led by a high profile image and backed by much general information targeted at as many groups and individuals as possible.

45. The acceptance of the light rail principle by the District Councils is an essential early goal, prior to detailed consideration of individual routes. Local Members of Parliament as well as MP's and Peers with transport interests should be included in the education process.

46. Education of the public can be a long process and almost certainly will not be completed before the pressure to publish a first route becomes overwhelming. Those affected by the route who have not been reached by the education programme are likely to object out of ignorance and an instinctive fear of the unknown. There have been several historical precedents for this reaction.

47. Residents groups will always appear to represent the majority, but this may well not be true. In one of Midland

Metro's most difficult areas only 466 out of 10000 inhabitants visited the exhibition bus. Of these only 90 returned a questionnaire of which 19 were for the scheme, 62 were against and 9 didn't know. Neither the residents group nor the promoting authority can tell how the remainder would vote and perhaps they have no opinion.

48. Until light rail is operating on a widespread basis in this country the basic problems of lack of understanding and consequent lack of public acceptance will be difficult to overcome. At the time of preparing this paper, the results of Midland Metro's 1989 public consultation campaign are not known. The monitoring of awareness and support suggests that we are winning the battles but whether we have won the war remains to be seen.

REFERENCE

1.   Light Rail Transit - a report by the Light Rail Transit Topic Group to the Passenger Transport Executive Group, September 1988.

11. Collecting the revenue – what fares, which tickets?

J. R. BAGGALEY, MCIT, Independent Consultant

SYNOPSIS. New Light Rail systems must cover a large part of their costs from fare revenue. They must do this and still charge fares which are competitive with other modes of transport. This paper explores some of the issues which influence fare levels and the cost of fare collection. The discussion concentrates on the derivation of a suitable fare structure because this is the least documented of the key elements of the total fares system.

THE ELEMENTS OF A FARES SYSTEM.

1. Four separate elements of a fares system can be identified as a framework for analysis. Each is important and all are interrelated.

* Fare structure;
* Fare levels;
* Fare collection;
* Fare avoidance.

Each of these elements is discussed in the paper, but there is a concentration on the relationship between the fare structure\fare level and the various characteristics of the market, in an attempt to outline a framework within which fares issues can be discussed rationally. In the analysis three terms are used very specifically in relation to pricing journeys:

* Value - the maximum amount a person is prepared to pay for a given journey.
* Cost - the total perceived cost of a journey based on valuing the time elements at the prevailing behavioural value of time.
* Fare (price) - The monetary charge for a public transport journey (included in the cost).

2. It must be emphasised that each new or improved LRT system will be different in the markets it is designed to serve, the competitive environment and the positive

attributes of the system. This paper cannot detail the specific mix of characteristics appropriate for a particular system but it is intended to indicate the factors which must be considered and to challenge some of the assumptions on which the present view of fares is based.

3. There is also one other vital point which all those involved in promoting transport should remember...the fare system is not the product. However the fare system can be critical to the passenger perception of the product, and as will be explained later fare levels may play a large part in determining wether there is a product at all in particular markets.

FARE STRUCTURE

4. The key to any fares system is the underlying structure. This is the framework which is used to relate individual fares to each other and to the market. Structures can be defined in various ways, by reference to geographic units of charging, by classifying passengers or journeys by some characteristic or by the way in which travel is "packaged" for pricing purposes (journey by journey, stored value tickets, area passes etc.). A completely defined fare structure will involve all three.

5. There are some key influences on the appropriate fare structure for a system:

* The way in which the market may be segmented for charging purposes;
* The underlying cost structure of the system;
* The alternatives (ie the form of the competition);
* The ability of the passenger to comprehend it.

6. Fares structures have evolved against a background in which other factors have had to be considered as well, not least of which have been politics and the limitations of equipment. There is now more freedom on both these counts and so it may be a good time to consider some underlying fundamentals. It is obviously now important for the fare structure to take more account of the characteristics of the passengers likely to use the system. There are a number of ways in which public transport passengers can be categorised to place them in "market segments" for this purpose:

* by the underlying purpose of their journey;
* by the frequency at which they use the system;
* by the length of the journey;
* by the time of day the journey takes place.

Market Segmentation by Purpose.
7. A concept which will be developed throughout the paper

is that passengers put a value on each journey made. This
derives from the premise that people usually travel for a
reason. The value that is derived from a journey depends on
what the passenger intends to do at the destination. In
theory fares can then be related to journey purpose with the
intention of maximising revenue from those journeys with a
high value.

8. The key factor for the operator is therefore the value
a passenger places on a particular class of journey. A
simple division may be as follows:

* High value - Journeys to work and school, journeys
  for important personal business, particularly
  medical purposes, crisis journeys .
* Medium value - Key shopping journeys and regular
  social/recreational visits.
* Low value - Extra social/recreational journeys and
  recreational shopping trips etc.

9. It is not easy to directly determine the purpose of a
journey when a passenger comes to buy a ticket. Most
operators in urban transport overcome this problem by
ignoring it. Alternatively time of travel is used as a
surrogate.

10. One key factor which this analysis highlights is that
there is a maximum cost which the passenger should be
prepared to pay. This is fixed by the upper limit of the
value a passenger places on a particular journey. If this
cost is exceeded the journey will not take place. This limit
will vary between passengers as well as between purposes.

Market Segmentation by Frequency.
11. Frequency of travel is an important concept when
appropriate fares structures are being considered. To be
rigourous frequency needs to be linked to the degree of
dependence on the particular system (ie the proportion of all
journeys which the passenger makes on the system in
question). These characteristics are defined by:

* How many different journeys does a person make in a
  given period;
* What alternatives has the passenger for each
  journey? and,
* What can the passenger afford?

12. These concepts are not used in conventional transport
demand models nor are they often used by transport operators
when collecting market research data. Both normally treat
each trip as an isolated incident. However from the point of
view of the fares system they are very important,
determining:

* the opportunities for selling travel in bulk;
* the scope for encouraging additional journeys by appropriate pricing mechanisms;
* the information requirements;
* the need to consider through or co-operative ticketing arrangements with other operators.

This last point is critical for a rail system which may not be sufficiently extensive to cater for the wide variety of journeys made by a particular person. The journeys which cannot be made on the system will need to use an alternative.

Segmentation by Journey Length.
13. Most graduated fares structures are based on the view that the market can be segmented directly by journey length. Three different concepts are involved :

* an attempt to relate pricing to what is perceived as the basis of the cost to the operator of providing for the journey;
* the opportunity to reflect expected income differences based on the location of the "home" end of the journey;
* the need to mirror the cost of alternative means of making the same journey.

14. Many urban transport systems started with a flat fare. Graduated fares were only introduced as journeys lengthened with the outward spread of cities. Over time this relationship between fare and distance has become to be seen primarily in terms of equating the fare to the amount of travel. The historic links with the value placed on the journey (because in general the longer journeys were made by people with higher incomes), and the cost structure of the only alternative (which was walking) have been lost.

15. Changes in the structure of urban areas, and the replacement of walking by car journeys significantly alter these relationships between distance and the market. A move towards a more market orientated fare structure requires clear examination of these factors.

16. The concept of the value of a journey has already been considered. This has been shown to be related more to purpose than to distance. The following paragraphs examine some characteristics of alternative means of making the journey, to see if distance related fares still have some relevance.

The Alternatives to rail.
17. For a new urban rail system there will be three main alternative ways of making the journey:

* Walking, mainly over short distances;
* Private car;
* Buses, mainly for passengers who do not have access to a car.

The way in which passengers perceive the cost of using the alternatives for the same journey has an important impact on the overall shape of the ideal fare structure.

18.   Each of the alternatives has specific characteristics:

* walking is free, but in terms of total cost (including time) there is a marked correlation with distance, with the cost rising steeply as distance increases,
* there are few directly perceived costs of using a car, fuel costs rise slowly with distance and are probably not perceived on a finely graduated incremental scale and the only direct cost is parking which is fixed (more or less) when the destination is chosen,
* bus fares are usually graduated by distance, and the total cost of travel will be similar to rail.

The cost of using any alternative means of transport is therefore related primarily to distance because the time taken is roughly proportional to distance. Fares graduated by distance do therefore find some theoretical justification even when considered in a market context.

Possible Fare structures

19.   The preceding paragraphs have demonstrated that there are a number of ways of categorising the market for transport. An appropriate fare structure for a given system can be shaped in response to this profile of the market so that fares are related to what the passenger will pay. Other factors also play a part, particularly when choices must be made to retain simplicity.

* The nature of the transport system, particularly the distinction between a single line and a network.
* The type of service offered, particularly the frequency.
* The fare structure on competing public transport modes.

20.   The various factors can be used to define a "shape" for the fare structure.

* The value of the journey, as derived from the journey purpose sets an upper limit on the cost of the journey. This implies that beyond a certain distance (which varies with purpose) there is no

point in graduating the fare.
* Below this distance the aim should be to keep the
  cost below that of the alternatives.
* At short distances the main alternative is walking.
  Because the cost of walking increases quickly with
  distance (walking is slow) there is scope to
  differentiate fares fairly finely by distance whilst
  still keeping sensible increments in the fare. The
  minimum fare does however require careful
  consideration as there is a point at which walking
  will always cost less than any alternative, even
  if no fare was charged.
* At some point, which depends critically on parking
  charges, the perceived cost of using a car (or if no
  car is available the bus) becomes less than that of
  walking. The fare structure can still be related to
  distance, but the distance increments should be much
  larger to reflect the low incremental cost of
  distance for most car users.
* Ultimately the cost of using a car equates to the
  value of the journey, at which point the scale
  should cease to be graduated.

21. Other factors are also important in urban areas, such
as the existence of alternative destinations, which may have
a higher or lower value for a given type of journey. These
reinforce the idea that a fairly coarse fares structure may
actually be the best for longer distance fares, relating the
fare more to a heirarchy of destinations rather than the
precise distance.

22. At this point the framework described relates to the
cost of a journey (ie time and fare/price). It sets an
envelope within which prices (fares) can be established.

FARE LEVELS

23. The fare structure provides a framework which must be
built on. This is done by assigning fare values to each of
the units of the structure, with appropriate variations to
take account of the various market segments which are
considered worth pricing separately. These fare values must
reflect a number of influences:

* The revenue target for the system;
* The cost of alternatives;
* The value of the journey being made;
* The prevailing level of fares in the area, which is
  not the same as the "cost of alternatives".

24. The revenue target is fixed by the system cost. Total
revenue must cover all operating costs plus those elements of
capital cost which are not met by grant. However it is not

then good practice to use average costs per passenger
directly as a reference point for fare levels because:

* the cost structure of most LRT systems is such that
  the marginal cost of carrying an extra passenger is
  almost zero;
* the average cost per passenger depends critically on
  the number of passengers;
* each passenger values the journey differently.

25.   The classic economic view of transport is that it is a
derived demand.   This has implications for pricing any
transport product.   In essence the cost of transport is added
to the cost of whatever activity is undertaken at the
journey's destination and a decision to travel is taken on
the basis of wether the activity is worth the total cost.
Because journeys are rarely made for their own sake the time
taken and all the other hassles of a journey add to the
perceived cost.   Alternative means of transport impose
different costs for the same journey

26.   The cost of the journey is determined by:

* The time taken, related to speed, access and waiting
  times;
* The fare or money spent directly;
* Comfort, which includes a wide variety of
  considerations including the ability to get a seat,
  the general environment, noise etc.
* Ease of use, where the perceived complications of
  public transport may be significant.

27.   The influence of the cost of alternative ways of
making a journey has already been discussed in relation to
the fare structure.   For any system to compete successfully
the total cost of a given journey must be less than that
imposed by using the alternatives.   For this equation to
balance the fare charged for public transport should be
derived by subtracting the other cost elements from the total
cost of travel using the most appropriate alternative.   It
should be noted that passengers do not pay for good
attributes in a positive way, it is simply that a good
service imposes fewer costs overall and so there is more
opportunity to charge a higher fare within the acceptable
limit for the overall cost.

28.   Over short distances walking is the main alternative.
It is difficult to put a cost on a walk because:

* Different people have widely different perceptions
  of the effort involved depending on their own
  abilities, the time available, and the weather;
* Walking is perceived as free, and therefore there is

a psychological barrier against paying directly for
a motorised alternative;
* The main cost of the public transport alternative is
the time spent waiting (not the travelling time) and
so the potential fare varies considerably depending
on the frequency offered;

29. What is clear however is that shorter distance fares
must acknowledge the cost of a walking (in terms of time
spent), which is low for the first few kilometres. To be
attractive fares must also be low or the journeys simply will
not be made.

30. The main alternative for all longer journeys in urban
areas is the private car. Motoring costs form an
uncomfortable ceiling for public transport fares because:

* most of the costs of car ownership and use are not
perceived at the time of use;
* the only directly perceived cost of a specific
journey is the parking cost.

31. Alternative public transport services must also be
considered when fares are set. The fares on these services
usually have little or no theoretical basis, having evolved
over many years. In some cases there must be doubts that
they even represent "what the market will bear" in that they
put the total cost of using public transport above that of
the alternatives. Fares are however used as an immediate
comparison between competing services. This must be
acknowledged in the fare levels, although there may be merit
in challenging the established order if this allows fares to
be better matched to the current market.

32. A crucial factor which the earlier analysis has
highlighted is that the cost of a journey must be acceptable
in relation to the journey purpose, or else the journey may
not be made. Because the cost of a journey continues to rise
with distance, but the value does not, the fare that can be
charged effectively reduces (see para 27). In practice this
means that there is a limit beyond which higher fares are
counterproductive.

FARE COLLECTION

33. The fares set for the system must be collected from
passengers. Careful consideration must be given to the
revenue collection system because:

* It can become a significant cost item if poorly
designed and managed;
* It is usually a key point of contact between the
system and customers;

* The revenue collection system imposes constraints on
  the fare structure.

34. Some key point must be considered early in the design
because they have major implications for station layout and
may influence vehicle design:

* Are ticket sales going to be primarily self-service,
  and if so what manned sales are going to be
  available?
* Is some form of manual or automated entry/exit
  control system to be used to check that passengers
  hold valid tickets?
* Is there going to be a concentration on
  pre-purchased tickets?

35 There is now a general concensus of opinion in relation
to Light Rail systems that:

* Passenger self-service fare collection is the only
  cost effective method except at very low volumes
  where it may be possible to consider fare collection
  on vehicle, using the driver.
* Random checking of tickets both on and off vehicle
  is more cost effective than either manned or
  automated entry/exit controls except at very high
  passenger volumes.
* Pre-purchase is a valuable part of the fare
  collection system, but it must be carefully
  considered against the marketing philosophy of the
  system.
* There is a strong case for selling high value
  (pre-purchase) tickets from manned sales points to
  retain some personal contact with regular customers
  and to avoid the need to handle high value and
  potentially complex transactions automatically.

Designing the fare collection system.
36. The fares structure imposes many requirements on the
fare collection system, with key points being:

* The number of different fare values to be vended;
* The additional requirements involved in fare
  determination (eg time of day or day of week)
* The maximum value of ticket to be sold from any self
  service machine. (This determines the need for
  special payment facilities, eg note acceptors.)
* The length of time different tickets may be in
  circulation.
* The need to make payment facilities available to
  particular groups of potential users, particularly
  the disabled and children.

37.   These factors affect:

* The design of the vending machine;
* The number of units required;
* The complexity of the machine in terms of logic and also the number of actions the passenger needs to make to obtain a ticket;
* The ticket material and the additional security measures required for tickets valid for an extended period.

It is important to implement the chosen fares structure in the simplest possible way.   This should leave scope for introducing more variety into the fare structure without risking a loss of passenger comprehension.

38.   The key to implementing a good revenue collection system lies in attention to detail through the design and installation, involving such factors as:

* equipment reliability;
* location of equipment in relation to passenger activity;
* avoiding unnecessary actions by the passenger;
* instructions and fares information.

39. It perhaps is important to emphasise that reliability is crucial particularly with a self-service system.   It can be expensive to install cheap, unreliable fare collection equipment because not only is extra maintenance cost incurred but also revenue is lost whilst repairs are effected. Passengers can also quickly lose confidence in the system and so the long term damage can be substantial.   To avoid this there must be a commitment to repair equipment quickly, which in turn requires that faults are monitored.

FARE AVOIDANCE

40. Some passengers will try to avoid paying their fare either because they feel that it is socially acceptable to do so or because they do not feel the journey is worth the fare. Any system must accept a level of fare evasion but no system can allow fare evasion to become significant.   Some relevant factors are discussed in the following paragraphs.

41. The fare structure can influence the level of fare evasion significantly. Two features seem to be of particular relevance:
* the price of the cheapest ticket, as this is often purchased by those who do not wish to pay the full amount but who do not wish to risk travelling without a ticket entirely:
* the increment between fares, as if this is large

there may be a reluctance to pay the extra "for just
one more stop".

Other significant factors are the ease with which genuine
mistakes can be made and the variety of excuses which can be
offered particularly in relation to age related concessions.

42. By far the most significant factor is the extent to
which passengers perceive the revenue protection effort of
the operator to be credible. This involves several factors:

* there must be a highly visible presence of revenue
  protection staff;
* action must be seen to be taken against offenders,
  even where this may conflict with a user friendly
  image;
* deterrent penalties must be imposed, preferably on
  the spot;
* swift action should be taken whenever there is a
  significant increase in evasion.

However this revenue protection effort must be cost effective
too. There is an optimum level of activity for any system
which depends on the fare structure (para 41), the social
environment, the type of service operated and the fare
collection system.

43. The key to good revenue protection, and system
security generally, is good management. These activities
must not be allowed to become peripheral to more "exciting"
tasks.

APPLICATION

44. The preceding paragraphs have set out some pointers to
the development of a successful fares system for a new
transport system. Because each system is different it is not
possible to give a standard formula which can be adopted in
all cases. There are however some general strands that
emerge.

The market.
45. Potential passengers travel for a wide variety of
reasons and a critical decision for any transport provider is
the extent to which all these needs are or can be met by any
one system. This is a major determinant of the fares and
service level policy for the system. As it affects all
aspects of the design it must be taken at an early stage.

46. Fares are linked to the type of service being provided
as they can have a significant impact on the potential volume
of business. Because the cost structure of rail systems is
fairly insensitive to volume there is a strong positive link

between unit costs per passenger and volume.

Fare structure

47. There is evidence to suggest that the fare structure for a system carrying passengers for a mixed range of purposes and over a wide range of distances should adopt a fare structure which:

* has fairly fine graduations at short distances to reflect the price of the main alternative (walking);
* uses coarser graduations for middle and longer distance journeys, mirroring the relatively flat cost curve of the private car and the need to simplify the fares structure to make the system appear more user friendly;
* has a maximum fare, which may vary considerably by time of day, to reflect the maximum value a passenger can derive from a journey.

48. Obviously these general principles will need to be modified for particular systems. If there are few short distance passengers a simplified approach to short distance fares may be appropriate for example.

49. This general structure should apply to all types of ticket to avoid confusion and to give consistency in pricing. This helps in the identification of objectives for particular types of ticket.

50. Each type of ticket should have a clear purpose within the charging framework. The format adopted should be appropriate to the market particularly if the market has diverse travel patterns.

Fare levels.

51. There is a view that higher fares will help to fund much of the new investment in public transport. Some of the evidence points in a different direction, suggesting that in the medium and long term high fares are counterproductive. Given the competitive marketplace and the cost structure of a rail system compared with the competition there may be many cases where the road to financial stability comes through a low price high volume market, which is precisely the market railways developed in the first place.

52. However the cost of specific provision can and should be passed on to those customers who benefit from it, provided:

* the resulting charging structure remains comprehensible;
* the premium fare can be enforced; and
* the net result is not to drive away passengers at

other times as well.

Fare collection

53. More definite guidance can be given on this topic as the trends are clearer and the differences between alternatives more marked. Unless passenger flows are very heavy, which is unlikely except on a few systems in the UK, there is no general case for barrier control at stations, either manual or automated. There is however an overwhelming case for passenger self service for ticket sales.

54. Despite this strong concensus regarding the most appropriate form of fare collection equipment there is still insufficient attention paid to the implementation of such systems. Good design, in the fullest sense of the word, is essential to the success of automated fare collection.

55. Self service fare collection does not imply "no staff" fare collection. A successful scheme requires policing well. However the staff can be mobile and flexible resulting in:

* better supervision of the system as a whole;
* lower staff overheads at low volume times;
* the ability to police a wider range of fares and ticket types, including those which can only be policed on train (eg 2-class services).

CONCLUSION

56. Fares are not a minor part of the implementation of a successful light rail system. They affect:

* the type of service which may be viable;
* the level of demand at different times of day;
* the equipment needed to sell tickets, and hence the design of stopping places;
* the staff necessary to ensure that revenue is collected; with a major impact on running costs.

57. Early and detailed consideration must be given to all the issues, with a full understanding of the implications of a particular course of action. There must also be consistency throughout the process:

* the fare structure and fare levels must be appropriate to the market and the chosen service strategy;
* the revenue collection system must be consistent with the fare structure, the types of ticket offered and the characteristics of the passengers;
* station design, information provision and system staffing must be consistent with the revenue collection system.

165

12. Environmental impact: problems and opportunities

J. RINGER, DipTP, MRTPI, AILAM, and M. DAY
Environmental Resources Limited

Introduction

This paper examines the application of Environmental Assessment (EA) to the development of Light Transits Systems (LTS). It is suggested that EA represents a dual opportunity for LTS developers;

-   it enables developers to avoid creating unnecessary environmental disturbance and to identify and to mitigate those impacts which cannot be avoided;

-   it makes it easier for developers to demonstrate the nature and scale of the environmental benefits of LTS over alternative forms of public transport.

EA, as practised in the UK, is described as the environmental planning considerations in LTS design and route selection. The major environmental disturbances inherent in all large scale public transport systems are detailed and the significance of the types of impacts caused by LTS are assessed against that of impacts associated with competing systems.

In establishing the role of LTS in the spectrum of public transport options, the conclusions of the 1979 Helsinki Congress[1] have been followed. This referred specifically to Light Rapid Transport (LRT) systems. It has been assumed for the purposes of this paper that similar principles apply to both LTS and LRT, namely:

-   light rail is seen as a complement to other systems;

-   light rail is a rail borne form of transport, ranging from tram to rapid transport system, on its own right of way, underground or on embankments or viaducts;

-   light rail capacity is between bus and railway and therefore is particularly suitable for the improvement of public transport in medium sized cities;

-   light rail is flexible for conversion to tramway or metropolitan railway;

-   light rail improves the flow of public transport and makes cities more human;

- light rail is more acceptable in environmental terms than most of the alternatives.

Structure of the Paper

The paper is set out as follows:

o   **Environmental Assessment:** The current status of EA in the British planning system is explained. The process of EA is briefly described and the required content of an Environmental Statement (ES) is given.

o   **LTS and the environment:** The methods used to establish the magnitude of environmental impact are described as are the implications these have for LTS route selection.

o   **Description of major environmental issues:** The major environmental issues raised by all public transport systems are described. The scale of the impacts caused by LTS, compared with the scale of those arising from alternative public transport systems is assessed in each case.

o   **Recommendation for environmental planning in LTS development:** The procedures recommended for efficient environmental planning in LTS are listed.

o   **Conclusions:** The main conclusions of the paper are summarised.

Introduction of Environmental Assessment

The Department of the Environment refers to the technique as Environmental Assessment and their terminology is followed in this paper. Environmental Assessment, to quote a recent DoE booklet[2] "is an important technique for ensuring that the likely effects of new development on the environment are fully understood and taken into account before the development is allowed to go ahead".

The technique is not a new one and experience of carrying out EA over many years has lead to general agreement that the four essential tasks accomplished by a successful EA are:

-   Prediction of impact magnitude: The scale or size of the various environmental disturbances is estimated;

-   Prediction of impact significance: The importance of the predicted impact in relation to current societal values is assessed;

-   Determination of mitigation measures: The measures which will be taken to remedy or alleviate the significant impacts are described and justification given as to why any residual impacts should or may not be mitigated;

-   Communication of results: An Environmental Statement is produced describing the study and including the data necessary to assess the impacts. This Statement should include a non-technical summary[3].

Box 1: Annex III of the EIA Directive

---

1. Description of the project, including in particular:

    -   a description of the physical characteristics of the whole project and the land-use requirements during the construction and operational phases,

    -   a description of the main characteristics of the production processes, for instance, nature and quantity of the materials used,

    -   an estimate, by type and quantity, of expected residues and emissions (water, air and soil pollution, noise, vibration, light, heat, radiation, etc) resulting from the operation of the proposed project.

2. Where appropriate, an outline of the main alternatives studied by the developer and an indication of the main reasons for his choice, taking into account the environmental effect.

3. A description of the aspects of the environment likely to be significantly affected by the proposed project, including, in particular, population, fauna, flora, soil, water, air, climatic factors, material assets, including the architectural and archaeological heritage, landscape and the inter-relationship between the above factors.

4. A description of the likely significant effects of the proposed project on the environment resulting from:

    -   the existence of the project,

    -   the use of natural resources,

    -   the emission of pollutants, the creation of nuisances and the elimination of waste;

    and the description by the developer of the forecasting methods used to assess the effects on the environment.

5. A description of the measures envisaged to prevent, reduce and where possible offset any significant adverse affects on the environment.

6. A non-technical summary of the information provided under the above headings.

7. An indication of any difficulties (technical deficiencies or lack of know-how) encountered by the developer in compiling the required information.

In performing the above it is important not to waste time and resources unnecessarily. Therefore a "scoping" exercise should be completed. In scoping, the key parameters for investigation are established by consultations and brief preliminary investigation. This ensures that time and resources are correctly focused in the main study. EA does not require "a study of everything".

The EC Directive

The European Community Directive 337/85/EEC was accepted by the Council of Ministers in July 1985[4]. It allowed member states three years in which to introduce Environmental Assessment into development control procedures for "projects which are likely to have significant effects on the environment". The projects concerned are listed in annexes to the Directive. Annex I is a list of nine kinds of major development for which an EA must always be performed. Annex II is a list of developments for which EA may be necessary "where Member States consider that their characteristics so require and covers a far wider range of development". An LTS would fall under Annex II 10(g); "Tramways, elevated and underground railways, suspended line or similar lines of a particular type used exclusively or mainly for passenger transport".

Annex III of the Directive sets out the information which should be supplied by a developer in an Environmental Statement, this is reproduced in Box 1. Member States are given the discretion to relax these informational requirements if they consider that the particular stage of the development control procedure does not require them or that it would be unreasonably difficult for the developer to compile some part of the data. In this case the ES should contain at least the following information:

-    a description of the project comprising information on the site, design and size of the project;

-    a description of the measures envisaged in order to avoid, reduce and, if possible, remedy significant adverse effects;

-    the data required to identify and assess the main effects which the project is likely to have on the environment;

-    a non-technical summary of the above information.

Implementation of the EC Directive in the United Kingdom

EC Directives do not have legal force on the citizens of the member state. They must be implemented by amending existing national law or introducing new legislation.

The large majority of development types listed in the EA Directive already require consent under existing legislation. The UK governments strategy therefore has been to augment relevant legislation with sets of regulations, over 20 of which have so far been introduced.

Most projects requiring EA in the UK also require planning permission under the Town and Country Planning Act (1971). The regulations amending this are the most detailed[5] and are supplemented with an explanatory circular[6] and a booklet[2] produced by the Department of the Environment. These detail, respectively, how to interpret and to apply the Regulations, and how an environmental statement should be prepared. The Circular advises that EA will be necessary for Annex II projects in three main types of cases:

(i)   for major projects which are of more than local importance;

(ii)   occasionally for projects on a smaller scale which are proposed for particularly sensitive or vulnerable locations;

(iii) in a small number of cases, for projects with unusually complex and potentially adverse environmental effects, where expert and detailed analysis of those effects would be desirable and would be relevant to the issue of principle as to whether or not the development should be permitted.

A developer can seek to obtain consent for an LTS scheme via a private act of parliament. As a consequence the TCP Regulations would not apply, nor would any others currently in force. Indeed the EC Directive specifically excludes from its provisions projects "adopted by a specific act of national legislation" (article 1.5).

The Joint Select Committee on Private Bill Procedure, however, proposed in their report of Autumn 1988 that each House of Parliament should amend its standing orders to require an environmental statement to be deposited with any Bill to approve a project requiring assessment under the Directive but for this provision[7]. This was accepted by the Government and, although no change to standing orders has yet been made, the DoE booklet on EA procedures[2] informs the reader that "It is the Government's view that where, but for this provision, environmental assessment would have been required for a project, the promoter of a Bill should provide an environmental statement which can be considered by the select and standing committees of each House on the Bill.

Reasons for LTS Developers to Undertake EA

As UK law currently stands EA is not required for LTS developments which are to be the subject of private Bills. Environmental considerations however are increasingly becoming key determinants of the acceptability of projects. Therefore, given that environmental information must be gathered and analysed, efficient techniques must be developed to do this. EA is an instrument with a proven track record. After the initial phase of its development, the Environmental Protection Agency reports that US experience has been that EA can actually lead to cost savings[8]. British developers have also found this[9]. Other advantages are that when using EA developers have access to a well developed set of methodologies developed by past and continuing international research. In Britain some developers have long been aware of the advantages of EA and many voluntary ESs have been submitted which predated, or fell outside the jurisdiction of, regulations implementing the EC Directive.

Examples of these include four in which ERL has participated in the preparation of the ES:

- The Channel Tunnel project 1987;

- The South Warwickshire Prospect Open Cast Mine (1987);

- The European Rail Link project, for British Rail;

- Extension of the Jubilee Line, for London Regional Transport (1989).

All of these sought to obtain consent through the Private Bill procedure.

The reasons why LRT developers should undertake or commission EA can therefore be summarised as follows:

- EA is, often required for projects subject to planning control, and may soon become a mandatory adjunct to parliamentary bills;

171

- EA procedures provide an efficient way to collect, analyse and present environmental information;

- EA will help demonstrate the environmental advantages of LTS over alternative forms of urban public transport.

Production of an Environmental Statement

LTS, even if it is more acceptable in environmental terms than the alternatives, still may have significant impacts on the environment. To achieve maximum benefit and to reduce the risk of environmental damage, a number of steps should be taken:

o   Establish the scale of projected operational service, based on carrying capacity and speed, and select the appropriate form of vehicle system.

o   Establish the specific engineering implications of a particular route or series of routes.

o   Then assess the likely environmental impact arising; from those engineering implications and from the selection of vehicle system.

o   Demonstrate that environmental matters have been assessed at the following stages;

- **pre-qualification;** this should give a marketing advantage over rival bids and should highlight key issues for the decision makers.

- **tender;** all of the important environmental impacts should be identified in a submission, many of these impacts will be controversial and may require detailed consultation.

- **design;** clients and Parliament may expect that the design of a particular proposal includes the preparation of an environmental statement, which makes clear the environmental implications and which allays concerns and avoids adverse impacts.

Selecting a Route for LTS

Having now selected a route for a proposed LTS a number of points are worth bearing in mind:

o   An assessment of the environmental implications of an LTS involves an appreciation of engineering design and vice versa.

o   An engineering design and its associated environmental implications are directly related; alterations of that design in turn alters the scale and nature of potential environmental impacts.

o   Based on experience of producing ES for the European Rail Bill and for the Jubilee Line extension the following matters are likely to be the most significant environmental issues;

- changes in noise levels;

- visual impacts;

- air quality impacts;

- impacts on other traffic;

- safety; and

- socio economic impacts.

Each of these matters is therefore now discussed in greater detail in this paper.

Noise

Introduction

The principal environmental issue associated with passenger transport facilities, based on discussions with the local residents, is concern over the levels of noise generated during operation.

Effects of Noise

Noise has a number of specific and well defined effects as follows:

- annoyance;

- sleep disturbance;

- speech interference;

- startle effects.

Attitudes to Noise

The overall assessment of noise in the environment is not so straightforward in terms of what is acceptable. Consequently, attitudinal factors must be taken into account. For example, with regard to the exposure of people to train noise in 1972 it was estimated that approximately 38% of the population of England heard train noise but only 2% were bothered by it. These values compare with 89% and 23% respectively for road traffic noise.

Sources of Noise Impact:

There are two major sources of noise impact from an LTS; operational noise and construction noise.

Operational noise impacts:

The following is a list of __major__ operational noise impacts;

- the passage of passenger services, this may include vibration where properties lie over shallow tunnel sections.

- the passage of maintenance vehicles particularly from marshalling yards and sidings,

- the operation of stations e.g. public address system,

- the operation of electricity sub-stations (generation of continuous noises at frequencies twice the fundamental electric frequency).

Construction noise impacts:

The following is a list of the major construction noise impacts;

- the building of the track, stations and operational facilities,

- tunnelling operations (if applicable).

- the excavation and filling of land,

- vehicle movements.

Key Noise Impact:

The most significant, permanent, noise impact from an LTS system is likely to arise from the operation of the passenger service. To many local residents this may appear to be the most important single environmental impact. It may also be the cause of most of the local objections.

Three significant factors which contribute to the total noise from the operation of the passenger service are:

- the peak noise level based on the design of the trains, the condition of the rail, the type of superstructure and the speed of the vehicle,

- the frequency of the service.

- the duration of noise.

Mitigation of Peak Noise Levels

Peak noise levels may be reduced by a series of mitigation measures. However, mitigation should reflect all the environmental and engineering considerations. For example, the noise level in a particular area may be reduced by limiting the frequency of the service, however, a reduction in the frequency of the service may in itself impair the efficiency of the operational system, which in itself may be undesirable. It is important to recognise that a halving of the number of trains reduces the 24 hour Leq by only 3dB(A). The mitigation therefore has to be tailored to suit the appropriate circumstances. The following list of mitigation measures is therefore a list of possible tools or aids for reducing noise levels which are only appropriate in specific locations and in certain circumstances;

o   Put route in tunnel.

o   Move the alignment of the track.

o   Reduce speed of vehicle.

o   Reduce frequency of service.

o   Reduce peak noise levels by altering the engineering design e.g.

-    introduce continuously welded track (which is standard on most new systems);

-    avoid signalling systems which use block joints;

-    introduce rubber tyred systems;

-    careful design of viaducts;

-    reduce the height of elevated sections (this may be a disbenefit to those closest to the track);

-    introduce ballasted track;

o   Reduce peak noise levels by altering the engineering design of the car as follows;

-    reduce wheel radiation by introducing rubber elements between the rim and the wheel;

-    provide noise and vibration absorbers on the wheel;

-    reduce wheel squeal by introducing wheel flanges or rail lubricators on curved track;

-    reduce propagation and emission using noise reduction mats, deeper body skirts, noise screens;

-    reduce noise from traction motors and gears;

-    reduce noise from the auxiliary equipment, e.g. compressors, air conditioning.

Possible Effects of Mitigation

Each mitigation measure has a specific effect in reducing noise levels and the following are guides[4] to those likely effects.

Modification	Enhancement over ideal CWT track
Joint track	+ 5 dB(A)
Slab tack (ie. unballasted)	+ 4 dB(A)

Slab track, Viaduct	+ 7 dB(A)
Ballastless, Steel Viaduct/Bridge	+10 dB(A)
Ballasted, Concrete Viaduct	+ 3 dB(A)
Ballasted, Concrete Viaduct with Resilient Membrane	0 dB(A)
Rail corrugations	up to +15 dB(A) depending on severity

These modifications assume that use is made of continuously welded track (CWT), without corrugations, is laid on wooden or concrete sleepers, on level and open ground with a bed of ballast below.

Conclusion

Noise impacts from LTS are likely to be less annoying than noise from alternative forms of transport, such as buses. The noise impact depends upon local circumstances and the level of mitigation that can be introduced. It is easier to introduce noise mitigation to an LTS than to an existing road, because of the flexibility of LTS.

Visual Impacts

Introduction

Two types of impact may need to be assessed:

- visual impacts i.e. impacts on the visual amenity of observers; and

- townscape impacts i.e. impacts on the character of the townscape.

Visual

Visual impacts may result from the loss of existing views, from the opening up of new views due to changes in townscape, from a reduction in the quality of existing views, or from intrusion into existing views.

Townscape

Townscape impacts may result from changes to key elements which contribute to the character and quality of the area. These elements include the scale of external spaces, the form and style of buildings and the prominence of existing transport infrastructure.

Scale of Visual Impact

The choice of mode for public transport service depends on the following:

- the anticipated demand for that service;

-       the speed required.

Once the type of operational system has been determined then the scale of visual impact can be predicted with reasonable accuracy. If, for operational reasons, it is decided to adopt a Metro system, with a relatively high carrying capacity then it follows that the overhead masts are likely to be large. It follows therefore that Metro systems are typically visually more intrusive than a lightweight tram which has a much smaller carrying capacity.

Sources of Visual Impact

Depending upon the scale of the system and the size of vehicles to be used, the following permanent visual impacts are likely to arise:-

o   The infrastructure itself, including:

        -       overhead electrical masts and wires;

        -       viaducts, bridges, elevated tracks, cuttings and embankments;

        -       tunnel portals, ventilation shafts, marshalling yards, stations and electrical sub-stations;

        -       vehicles.

All the above impacts are of a permanent nature. The significance of their impact however, is likely to decrease over time as they become an established feature of the local townscape.

Construction

Visual impacts may also arise from construction work and from a need to mitigate other impacts, for example noise. Noise walls, barriers or fences in themselves may create a significant impact in a local area. Similarly the location of construction camps and construction sites is only likely to have a temporary, local impact but may be just as controversial as the engineering works.

Proposals to Reduce Visual and Townscape Impacts

A number of general measures can be introduced to reduce visual and townscape impacts as follows:

o   Creation of bunds to screen intrusive views.

o   Place route in tunnel or move alignment of the track.

o   Tree and shrub planting to improve the appearance of features such as embankments.

o   Adoption of high standards of design for all engineering features especially;

-       bridges, raised superstructures and overhead electrical equipment;

-       design sympathetic to the townscape including use of attractive local materials for facing viaducts and other structures.

Conclusion

The impact of LTS on the character of the townscape and in particular visual intrusion from overhead equipment in historic city centres may create an environmental disbenefit, however because of the flexibility of LTS then appropriate mitigation may be introduced to reduce that impact, for example by tunnelling under a historic city centre.

Air Quality

Introduction

Amongst the principal benefits of LTS, over comparable forms of transport and particularly in busy city areas, is the associated reduction in vehicle emissions and the consequent reduction in air pollution. Where LTS displaces cars there should be an attendant reduction in the following pollutants locally:

Nitrogen dioxides (NO)

The two main sources of nitrogen dioxides in the UK are power stations (40%) and road traffic (40%). Concentrations of NO are thus generally related to the proximity and quantity of these sources to any particular location.

Oxides of Carbon (CO, CO^2)

The greatest source of CO in the UK is from motor transport. Approximately 90% of atmospheric CO in the UK is emitted by vehicles. For this reason ambient CO concentrations at any location are directly related to distance from nearby roads and numbers of vehicles travelling on these roads. CO^2 is harmless for human health but is a major 'greenhouse' gas.

Lead (Pb)

With an increasing trend in the use of unleaded petrol, it is likely that ambient lead levels will continue to fall particularly in the centres of urban areas, however, concentrations of lead are highest in areas frequented by motor transport.

Hydrocarbons

Petrol engines are an important source of hydrocarbons, which in some cases have direct effects on human health and plants. Some of them are also reactive and play a crucial role in the formation of photochemical oxidants as found in urban 'smogs'.

Particulates

Diesel engines are a significant source of urban 'smoke'; - largely contaminated carbon particles.

Odours

Unburnt hydrocarbons and those resulting from partial or incomplete combustion produce odours and irritants which are considered to be nuisance pollutants. Odour intensities are usually greater for diesel engines than petrol engines.

Air Quality Impacts from Construction

A major potential source of air quality impacts may arise during the construction phase and relate to possible dust emissions. Dust emissions are likely to arise from the following activities during construction as follows;

- site preparation and clearance works;

- demolition of buildings;

- earth moving operations, spoil storage and use of construction materials (e.g. sand)

- airborne pollution from construction vehicle emissions and from on site fuel storage.

Airborne dust from construction activities is of generally larger particle size, is emitted from low elevations and is therefore rapidly deposited close to source.

Sources of Impact

In assessing the impacts of LTS on air quality it is noticeable that all of the related impacts are of no great significance except during the construction phase. It is important to recognise, however, that these construction impacts are typical of any major engineering works.

Of the direct impacts from the operation of LTS there are only two minor sources of impact as follows:

- release of particles from the braking system

- emission of ozone from arcing.

(The production of electricity from power stations, and its subsequent use in operating the system, is an indirect impact which should be assessed).

Conclusion

In terms of a direct comparison between an LTS and a comparable motor related passenger transport system, in so far as air quality is concerned, then the LTS is streets ahead and has dramatically less impact. An important point to stress here, however, is that the reduction in emissions due to reduced road traffic arising from the operation of the ES must be quantified to identify the environmental benefits of this.

Impacts on Other Traffic

Introduction

The introduction of LTS often involves some form of substitution of other traffic arrangement. This is especially true where street running is involved. Inevitably the effect of LTS will be to modify existing traffic flows particularly at congested locations. Experience of operating LTS is limited in this country, however, an assessment has been made of the operation of the Tyne and Wear Metro system and a report was produced in 1984 entitled "The Metro Report"[5] which set out some of the key findings of the Metro operation in terms of traffic conditions. A synopsis of those findings follows:

o   "The large scale reduction of bus movements in the central area has helped the road network to absorb traffic growth while maintaining an improved level of performance: between 1980 and 1984 average car journey speeds in Newcastle city centre increased by about 20%.

o   "While releasing central area road space for private transport, the Metro has also attracted journeys that would otherwise have been made by car: since the introduction of the integrate system, the growth in car traffic in the central area has been 3% - 4% less than in the outer area."

o   "Fewer bus movements in the central area have meant fewer road accidents, particulary for pedestrians."

o   "In a number of centres the pattern of pedestrian movement has changed in response to the Metro and related bus routeing."

o   "Pedestrian flows in the northern part of Newcastle city centre, particularly around Monument and Haymarket stations, have increased substantially."

o   "Over 1 million journeys a year are made by park and ride Metro passengers, especially trips to and from the central area; about 10% of Metro passengers interviewed in 1984 used a car at one end of their journey."

Sources of Impact

The Tyne & Wear Metro system was designed to use predominately existing British Rail tracks with the addition of new tunnels to reach the City Centre and provision of a new bridge over the River Tyne. Other proposals for LTS including the Greater Manchester, Sheffield and South Yorkshire projects involve operations on existing highway where the impacts on other traffic is direct and clearly more significant.

Where street running is required there will be permanent impacts on the following:

- private vehicular transport;

- existing public transport (particularly buses);

- service vehicles;

- pedestrians;

- the disabled.

Conclusion

LTS can help to encourage greater use of cities by pedestrians, can assist in reducing dependence upon cars; both of which maybe considered environmental benefits.

Safety

Introduction

Safety is an important consideration in any transportation system and with LTS the responsibility of protecting 'the passenger' rests with the operator, whereas the similar decision made to travel by car is made by an individual who then takes personal responsibility for his or her safety.

One conclusion of the 'Metro Report' was that "Fewer bus movements in the central area have meant fewer road accidents, particularly for pedestrians".

Clearly the fact that pedestrian flows in the northern part of Newcastle have increased substantially, indicate that Metro has helped to produce a situation where people are making greater use of the City Centre. It could therefore be argued that Metro is making the City Centre of Newcastle more accessible to the pedestrian and therefore more human. A feeling of safety is part of this overall process.

Sources of Impact

The likely impact of LTS on safety could be considered in two broad categories: direct and secondary.

Direct Impacts

Direct impacts are concerned with the location of new infrastructure and the operation of existing services.

New infrastructure impacts cover:

- new rights of way, embankments, viaducts and other engineering structures;

181

- shared rights of way and creation of new points of direct conflict.

Existing service impacts include:

- substitution of existing motor traffic rights of way;

- reorganisation of existing traffic management arrangements;

- removal of accident black spots.

Secondary Impacts

Secondary impacts may result from decision made because of changes in accessibility, e.g. the following:

- increased commuting on public transport;

- increased use of city centres by pedestrians;

- improved access for the disabled.

They may lead to:

- opportunities for other environmental improvements (e.g. pedestrianisation);

- a more acceptable degree of pedestrian accessibility in city centres, making them more 'human';

- greater city centre usage by 'at risk' groups such as women, young children, the elderly, and people with disabilities.

Mitigation Options

To a certain extent the scale of safety impacts is dependent upon overall planning controls within a particular area, and the need to integrate LTS with public buildings, shopping areas and offices. Ideally pedestrian only networks should dovetail with LTS. This should reduce the possible conflicts between LTS users and those travelling in cars or buses.

Conclusion

LTS can complicate safety provision by introducing another mode of transport which may conflict with the existing provision. In busy city centres, and particularly where LTS is segregated, as it is in Tyne and Wear, then it can lead to a reduction in the number of road accidents, particularly for pedestrians.

Socio-economic and Development Impacts

Sources of Impact

Socio-economic impacts could be considered in two broad categories: direct and secondary.

Direct Impacts

Direct impacts are concerned with new job creation in both the construction and operation phases.

o   Construction employment covers:

-     direct employment by contractors;

-     employment generated by first round orders for materials e.g. steel for rail line.

o   Operational employment includes:

-     operational crew;

-     station staff;

-     engineering staff;

-     service and maintenance staff.

Secondary Impacts

Secondary impacts may result from decisions made by workers and/or businesses because of accessibility changes stemming from LTS. They may include:

-     increased commuting to the central area;

-     in-migration of residents to an area;

-     new businesses moving in to an area;

-     increased tourism potential due to improved access.

They may lead to:

-     changes in house prices;

-     changes in wages and the job market.

Increased accessibility for commuters from place to place and for businesses may lead to pressures for development, and in consequence, to impacts on the environment which need to be assessed. These are likely to be focused around access points.

Conclusion

Of all the environmental effects examined the socio economic and development impacts are least directly related to the engineering design. Whereas noise, visual and air quality impacts are inextricably linked with the design, the socio-economic impacts are partly consequent upon the secondary impacts, which may result from decisions made by workers and or businesses.

Socio economic and development impacts can be manipulated by external factors and in particular by overall planning policies. In the case of the Tyne and Wear Metro the system was established in the context of the existing planning policies which placed great emphasis on an integrated public transport policy. External forces, such as the general state of the local and national economy, however, are probably the most important factors determining the land of socio-economic impacts.

Guidelines

Introduction

LTS should be able to stimulate the local economy and development providing it is integrated within existing planning policies and is used to compliment existing systems; particularly if it encourages public transport and makes cities more accessible. A number of guidelines may be worth noting as follows:

EA

Embark on a full EA of the preferred route.

Major Issues

Pay particular attention to noise, visual, traffic, and socio-economic impacts and demonstrate the environmental advantages in terms of improved air quality, safety and accessibility.

Consultation

Involve those who are affected by the proposal in detailed consultation at an early stage and maintain that consultation throughout.

Update Engineering Design

Integrate the environmental specialist and consultation manager into the engineering design process, review the designs and incorporate environmental mitigation as part of the ongoing process.

Reduce Direct Impacts on Property

Use LTS's ability to negotiate sharp curves and severe gradients, which may avoid costly, and potentially visually intrusive, civil engineering obstacles, to reduce property impacts.

Reduce Direct Impacts on People

Introduce mitigation measures, such as continuously welded track and noise walls, to reduce the most significant impacts of noise.

Reduce Direct Impacts on the Environment

Introduce high standards of design for all structures and re-use redundant (listed) structures wherever possible.

Integrate LTS Within the Existing Planning Framework

Dovetail the LTS proposal into the planning, land use and infrastructure framework and establish close relationships with the appropriate agencies, organisations and where appropriate the relevant individuals.

Ensure that the LTS is Accessible and Enjoyable

Introduce special facilities which address the needs of women, people with disabilities, the young and the elderly; open up views from the LTS; introduce features of interest for the benefit of passengers including an interpretation package; organise special trips.

Conclusion

Introduction

In assessing whether or nor the introduction of LTS is more desirable than the alternatives, in environmental terms, one should examine its benefits and impacts on the following:

- people;

- property;

- the natural environment.

People

The key potential benefits to people are as follows:

- reduction in air pollution;

- reduction in the level of noise;

- improvement in safety - particularly for pedestrians;

- improved accessibility to opportunities;

- reduction in visual intrusion where the use of gradient capability can be made to dive under or climb over congested road junctions and other traffic obstacles;

- the avoidance or deferment of costly and environmentally damaging road schemes.

The key impacts on people are as follows;

- potential increase in noise levels at specific locations;

- potential visual impact from overhead equipment;

- possible interruption of vehicular traffic flows;

- displacement from homes.

Property

The key potential benefits to property are as follows:

- reduction in property loss and avoidance of damage to the townscape, due to ability to negotiate sharp curves and severe gradients;

- improvement in residential property values;

- improvement in retail, office and leisure property values;

- improvement in access to social and cultural facilities for a wider cross section of the population;

The most severe impacts on property are likely to be:

- potential for blight of residential properties close to a 'preferred' or agreed alignment;

- the introduction of overhead equipment, particularly in historic city centres;

Natural Environment

The key potential benefits to the natural environment include:

- avoidance of land take due to the ability to negotiate sharp curves and severe gradients;

- avoidance of air pollution emissions;

- the opportunity to undertake sympathetic environmental enhancement projects e.g. Metro lineside landscaping.

The most severe impact to the natural environment is likely to be:

- the loss of land and damage to important or sensitive habitats.

Environmental Benefits

In environmental terms then the introduction of LTS has a number of significant benefits over the possible alternatives. To highlight these advantages it is important that the role of environmental evaluation begins at the proposal stage of a project when pre- qualification begins; continues into the tender stage and may even be a part of the tender process; is maintained through the evaluation of options into final design and implementation. It represents a very small element of the total project budget and may make the difference between winning a proposal and being consigned to the list of also rans.

References

(1)   The Helsinki Congress, 1979.

(2)   Department of the Environment, (1988a). Environmental Assessment, a guide to the procedures. Department of the Environment, 1989. HMSO London.

(3)   Wood, C. and N. Lee, (1988). The European Directive on Environmental of the Environment, 1989. HMSO London.

(4)   Commission of the European Communities, (1985). Council Directive of 27 June 1985 on the assessment of the effects of certain public and private projects on the environment. Official Journal of the European Communities L175, 40-48.

(5)   Department of the Environment, (1988b). The Town and Country Planning, (Assessment of Environmental Effects) Regulations 1988. HMSO, London.

(6)   Department of the Environment, (1988c). Circular 15/88. Environmental Assessment. HMSO, London.

(7)   HMSO, 1988. Report of the Joint Committee on Private Bill Procedure. HC Paper 97. HMSO, London.

(8)   Wathern, P. (1988). The EIA Directive of the European Community. In: EIA Theory and Practice, P. Wathern (Ed). Unwin Hyman.

(9)   Ends Report (1979). The British Gas Corporation: EIA and the cost of industrial development. Ends Report 34 8-9.

13. Light transit systems, parliamentary procedures and options

C. CLAYDON, Vice-President, Light Rail Transit Association

SYNOPSIS. Any new light rail transit or similar system requires Parliamentary authority for its construction and operation. The reasons for this are identified and the methods by which such authority may be obtained are reviewed. The most apposite method, the private Bill procedure, is examined in depth. Proposals for changes in this procedure were recently put forward by a Parliamentary Committee and their recommendations are also considered.

1.   The title adopted for this paper includes the expression "Light Transit Systems", a term which besides embracing rail transport is also apt to cover guided bus-ways and allied transport modes. I shall indeed be touching on some of these special modes, but for the most part attention will be concentrated on traditional rail systems. Even here, the nomenclature is diverse: railways, light railways, tramways, tramroads, rapid transit, light rapid transit, light rail transit. I will endeavour to explore the distinctions between these modes in due course, but where it is not necessary to differentiate, I trust that it will not ruffle susceptibilities if I use the long-standing generic term "tramway".

2.   In order to construct and operate a tramway in Great Britain it is usually necessary to secure prior statutory authority. In limited instances it is possible to avoid the need to obtain statutory powers - principally where a line is laid entirely on private land with the consent of the landowner. But such instances are obviously rare, especially since the mere crossing by the line of a public road or footpath at grade is sufficient to attract the need for statutory sanction.

3. Why should this be so? The main reasons for needing statutory powers are as follows:

3.1 To obtain immunity from actions for nuisance. The courts have long held that the installation of rails in the public highway and the use of flange-wheel vehicles on them without statutory authority constitute indictable nuisances.

3.2. To secure powers to acquire land compulsorily. It is in the nature of things that there are always some landowners who will refuse to sell land voluntarily at a reasonable price for the site of a line or for associated purposes such as sites for workshops, depots and electrical substations. Certain bodies, such as local authorities and passenger transport executives, possess limited powers of compulsory acquisition subject to Ministerial consent.

3.3. To authorise interference with public rights, such as the diversion or closure of public highways, public footpaths and the like.

3.4. To authorise interference with works or apparatus of public utilities - that is the pipes, ducts and cables of water, sewerage, gas, electricity and telephone undertakings. It frequently happens that there is need to divert or disturb these services when installing the rails, feeder cables and overhead line supports of a tramway system.

3.5. To enable enactments already governing parts of the tramway undertaking to be modified or repealed.

3.6. To gain the benefit of deemed planning permission for the proposed works. Tramway installations with statutory authority do not in general have to apply for planning permission as would otherwise be the case. This is by virtue of the Town and Country Planning General Development Order 1977, which confers deemed planning permission for such works.

4. There is another important consequence of installing a tramway system under statutory authority. It is thereby brought under the supervision of the Railway Inspectorate of the Department of Transport, the Government body charged with primary responsibility for overseeing the safe installation and operation of rail systems.

5. The acquisition of statutory powers for rail systems has a long history. For railways the story began in 1758, when powers were secured to install and operate a line in Leeds. This established the pattern which has continued

ever since of obtaining statutory permission for specific
lines. From the 1840s there has been legislation to
control railways more generally. Thus the Railway
Inspectorate, already referred to, was established by an
Act in 1842. Although the term "railway" has never been
comprehensively defined in legislation, it has come to be
accepted that it applies to lines which are generally
segregated and fenced off from adjacent properties and
which usually rely for their operation on some measure of
signalling or other method of control.

6. The term "tramway" was first used in a non-passenger
context - as referring to minerals, docks and contractors'
lines. But tramways in the modern sense of the term -
namely as a passenger-carrying transport mode usually
operating along public highways - were introduced into
this country from the United States in 1860. The
legislative pattern set by railways was soon followed.
Accordingly, private Acts were passed in relation to
specific lines, to be followed, in 1870, by a general
Tramways Act which regulated their operation and placed
them within the ambit of the Railway Inspectorate for
safety purposes. However, the expression "tramway" has
not been defined in any statute.

7. Somewhat later the term "tramroad" came into vogue
to bring out a useful distinction. "Tramway" was
thereafter generally taken to refer to a system in which
the rails were sunk into the ground, with only their
uppermost surface level with the adjacent highway or other
terrain, whereas the term "tramroad" was reserved for a
line in the nature of a railway in which the rails
projected above the surrounding land in such a way that
road vehicles were effectively inhibited from traversing
the same alignment. Then in 1896 Parliament passed the
Light Railways Act, which thus contributed another term,
again without definition but envisaged as something of a
cross between an ordinary railway and a tramway.

8. In more recent years other expressions have appeared
on the statute book. Thus the Tyneside Metropolitan
Railway Act 1973 used the expression "rapid transit system
of transport" to describe the lines which were to become
part of the Tyne and Wear Metro system. The Greater
Manchester (Light Rapid Transit System) Act 1988, as its
title suggests, employed the designation "light rapid
transit system" to describe the means of transport which
is to take over certain British Rail suburban lines in the
Manchester locality, linked by street running in the
central area. Finally, the South Yorkshire Light Rail
Transit Act 1988 provides for a system of "light rail
transit" to be introduced in and around Sheffield.

9. It is important to note however that useful though these modern expressions may be in terms of public presentation, they bear no intrinsic meaning of their own for legal purposes. Therefore when employed in legislation they have to be defined by reference to the hallowed terms "railway" or "tramway". So the 1988 South Yorkshire Act, for example, defines the expression "LRT system" in use throughout the statute as "the light rail transit system comprising the railways authorised by this Act, including the railways designated as tramways".

10. This holds true even for forms of transport which may be thought to offer little resemblance to either railways or tramways. For example, the Southampton Rapid Transit Bill currently before Parliament, which would authorise the installation of a "people mover" in that city, describes the vehicles to work the system as "rapid transit vehicles" and the infrastructure on which they are to operate as a "guideway". This latter term is defined as "an elevated or mainly elevated way which is supported on piers or embankments designed for the primary purpose of accommodating rapid transit vehicles and segregated from all road and rail systems". Somewhat surprisingly after that, clause 10 of the Bill goes on to provide that "For the purposes of the Regulation of Railways Act 1871 and Schedule 2 to the Telecommunications Act 1984 any such guideway is to be deemed a tramway".

11. It is perhaps convenient at this juncture to touch on the status of what may be compendiously described as "guided bus systems" in order to consider whether such systems require statutory authority for their installation and operation. I think that it has to be acknowledged that this is something of a "grey" area as far as the law is concerned. One of the difficult features is that the mode itself is protean in character. But the test is perhaps relatively simple: legislation is probably required if any of the reasons outlined at the outset of this paper are applicable. The following are instances where this would be the case:

11.1. If the surface of the highway would require modification in any of the following respects: by the laying in it of anything in the nature of a rail or rails; by the insertion in it of anything in the nature of a slot or trough; or by the installation in it of any other equipment which would project above the surrounding surface.

11.2. If compulsory powers are needed to acquire land or to divert the apparatus of other public utilities. Obvious examples would be when land is required for the site of the guideway or its supports or where it would be desired to place cables, conduits or other apparatus under the road surface or to plant posts along the roadside.

11.3. If sections of an existing highway were to be dedicated to the exclusive use of the new system as, for example, might be the case with a computer-controlled operation.

Otherwise it should be possible to proceed without statutory sanction. A recent example of such a case was the tracline experiment at Short Heath, Birmingham. The implementation of that system required nothing more for its infrastucture than kerbing which was somewhat higher than usual and which was installed with the agreement of the highway authority.

12. If therefore a would-be promoter of a rail system were to embark on the exercise of seeking statutory authority for his proposed installation, he would need to begin by categorising the proposed undertaking for legal purposes as a tramway or as a light railway or as an ordinary railway or as a combination of any of these, and adopt the procedures and statutory codes applicable to the mode or modes selected.

13. I turn now to a review of the possible options for securing such authority:

13.1. <u>The Tramways Act 1870</u>. A promoter may apply to the Secretary of State for Transport for a Provisional Order under this Act. The sensible idea behind this procedure is that if the promoter can convince the Secretary of State of the soundness of his case, the latter will then grant the Order, which although it has to be confirmed by an Act of Parliament, by what is known as a Provisional Order Confirmation Bill, the passage of the Bill through Parliament is likely to be purely formal. This is because the Department of Transport, not the promoter, is responsible for the conduct of the Bill. So apart from absolving the promoter from piloting the Bill through Parliament, there is a far greater chance that it will be allowed to pass without amendment. Before granting a Provisional Order, the Secretary of State may appoint an inspector to hold an inquiry into the proposals and to take account of the views of any objectors.

13.2. This procedure fell into disuse even at a time when tramways were flourishing in this country. This was principally because at that date most tramways were owned and operated by local authorities and the procedure was not available to them. Secondly, the procedure was not appropriate if compulsory acquisition powers were needed. Further, the Confirmation Bill itself could be petitioned against in Parliament, despite the fact that it was promoted by the Government. Finally, as the years passed, the 1870 Act inevitably became progressively more out-dated so that promoters required provisions outside the scope of the Provisional Order, which meant whether or not they were a local authority they had to seek other means to secure the powers which they needed.

13.3. <u>The Light Railways Acts 1896 and 1912.</u> A promoter may apply to the Secretary of State for Transport for a Light Railway Order under these Acts. Despite their title, these Orders are not limited to lines in the nature of railways. Light Railway Orders have been granted in respect of schemes which in their entirety involved street running. Furthermore, there is no limit legally to the speed at which vehicles may operate on such lines. The principal advantage of this procedure is that it normally requires no Parliamentary process, since the Secretary of State is able, if he is content, simply to confirm the draft Order as submitted by the promoter.

13.4. But of course things are rarely so simple. If there are objections, there is power to hold a public inquiry and this can clearly delay, or completely frustrate, the project. Moreover, the Secretary of State may not accede to the application if he is of the view that the magnitude of the proposal is such that it ought to be submitted to Parliament. In this event, he can make a Provisional Order which then requires confirmation by Parliament, where it can be petitioned against in the usual way. Also, although the Acts allow a Light Railway Order to confer powers of compulsory purchase, it is in practice not current Department of Transport policy to permit such powers to be included. Finally, an LRO does not carry with it deemed planning permission, so that a separate planning application is necessary. Given these considerations, it is unlikely that the procedure can be adopted for proposals of any great significance and indeed use of the powers is now largely confined to minor railway lines operated by enthusiasts.

13.5. <u>Private Bill.</u> A promoter may proceed by private Bill. This type of Bill is, if and when passed, like any other Act of Parliament save that it is of local, rather than general, application, affecting the interests of persons and bodies in a certain area rather than across the country as a whole. In theory, an Act of Parliament may provide for anything, and certainly this procedure is able to overcome many of the disadvantages of the other two methods. It can, for example, confer powers of compulsory acquisition, and outmoded requirements present in the other procedures can be up-dated and fine-tuned for the particular project. But this method is not without its disadvantages too. The following are perhaps the most important:

13.5.1. Bills may be deposited with Parliament only once a year - on or before 27th November.

13.5.2. Promoting a Bill can be an enormously complex undertaking. Detailed Standing Orders have to be observed and the procedural requirements and drafting of the Bill call for special skills. These tasks are performed by Parliamentary Agents and by Counsel drawn from the Parliamentary Bar. The provisions of the Bill have to be fitted into the matrix of the general law.

13.5.3. If street running is envisaged, the promoters may have an awkward dilemma. They must either incorporate in their Bill provisions taken from the Tramways Act (since it is the only legislative code governing this aspect) and so perpetuate outmoded features founded on that Act, or they must devise new provisions which, in an area where adherence to precedent is all important, provoke intense and usually unwelcome scrutiny of such departures from the norm.

13.5.4. The procedure can be expensive - perhaps amounting to well over £0.25 million in the case of an opposed Bill. Many of the same costs would be incurred whichever procedure were to be adopted - for example, fees for surveyors, engineers and cartographers, and for consultation, publicity and public information services. But fees are also charged by each House and there are the further fees payable to Counsel and the Parliamentary Agents.

13.5.5. The procedure can at times be subject to political interference. In the Commons, certain stages of a Bill's progress can be impeded simply by a single member shouting "Object!" Another development, following a pattern familiar in many other fields, enables small, but vociferous, pressure groups successfully to exert disproportionate influence given the largely passive attitude of the majority of peers and MPs.

14. It will be apparent from the foregoing that none of these methods for securing statutory powers is entirely suited to contemporary demands. And of these, only the private Bill procedure offers a realistic means of achieving the objectives of latter-day promoters. So we need to look a little more closely at the private Bill procedure, although only the barest outline of this complex process can be given in this paper.

15. A preliminary issue for determination is who may promote a private Bill. Is the power limited to passenger transport executives, or may local authorities do so? The answer is simple: anyone may promote such a Bill, even a private company or an individual. But of course if either Parliament or the Government does not think it appropriate for a particular body to undertake the operations proposed, then this will soon become manifest and it is unlikely that the measure will make much headway. This is clearly an issue to watch at a time when moves are afoot to divest municipalities of their transport functions.

16. Certain elements of the legislative process have already been touched on. There is thus the need to engage Parliamentary Agents (who are specially licensed solicitors) and Counsel. This is because when operating in this arcane field, it is necessary to employ those possessed of the requisite expertise. These advisers will elicit the promoter's requirements and translate them into Bill form (relying on precedent as far as possible). They have also to ensure that the Standing Orders of the two Houses, which govern the introduction and progress of the measure through Parliament, are observed. These Standing Orders normally require the consent of the local authority and highway authority to be obtained, and notices to be posted in the streets and on the lands which would be affected and also served on frontagers and railway and canal authorities affected. Certain Government Departments have also to be notified. Plans and gradient profiles of the proposed route have to be deposited and an estimate given of the cost of the works. Details of the gauge and motive power proposed have also to be given. Then the Bill itself has to be deposited by the due date.

17. After deposit of a Bill, there is a period during which Government Departments and bodies and individuals affected by the proposals are able to take up their concerns with the promoters with a view to seeing whether the provisions may be adjusted. Promoters may well be conciliatory to avert later opposition. Amendments may therefore be made to the Bill at this stage in order to meet these concerns. In this revised form, the measure is known as a "filled-up Bill". It then goes through the same stages as a public Bill: first reading; second

reading; committee stage; report stage; and third reading. This procedure has to be followed in both Houses and the House authorities decide by which House the Bill should first be considered. If one House amends a Bill after it has been approved by the other, it has to return to the first House for the amendments to be agreed there too.

18. Opposition to a Bill may be sustained despite concessions at an earlier stage. This may take two forms. Peers or MPs may seek to block its progress by motions to reject it or to amend it unacceptably at the second or third reading stages. Independent of such actions, individuals and bodies may oppose the Bill by lodging petitions against it or against particular clauses. Not everyone may petition - only those with the necessary locus standi may do so. These are, in the main, the persons who were served with notice of the Bill pursuant to Standing Orders. Government Departments may put in reports as an indication of their opposition.

19. Bills petitioned against or reported on in this manner are assigned to an Opposed Bills Committee and their progress may be materially checked while witnesses on behalf of the parties are examined, cross-examined and re-examined. Government Department representatives are not witnesses and may not be cross-examined, although the Chairman of the Committee may permit questioning. Again, as a matter of tactics, it is often prudent for promoters to meet the opposition by offering enhanced compensation or further amendments. This latter move often takes the form of a "second House undertaking" whereby the promoters agree to have the agreed amendment made in the other House. In this way, progress on the Bill may be expedited, but of course at a cost in financial terms or in terms of additional obligations or constraints.

20. Whether or not the Bill is opposed, its "Preamble has to be proved". This process requires witnesses to be called on oath to prove the correctness of the assertions recited in the Preamble to the Bill and any documents referred to therein have to be produced. This exercise provides the opportunity for the general objectives of the Bill to be scrutinised and receive endorsement, if such is the case. Ultimately, when the Bill has made its passage through all stages in both Houses, it receives the Royal Assent and so becomes an Act of Parliament.

21. It is perhaps instructive briefly to study the form and content of a typical Act. It begins with what is known as the Long Title, which summarises the scope of the enactment. There follows the Preamble, which recites why the Act is needed and the requirements which have been

observed. This is the Preamble which has to be proved.
Then follow the enacting words, which tell us that the
measure has the approval of Her Majesty and of both
Houses. We then come to the operative parts, which are
divided into Parts and Schedules. The Parts are divided
into "sections" which at the Bill stage are referred to as
"clauses". Part I is concerned with preliminary matters:
the Short Title (that is the title by which the Act will
be known); definitions; and the incorporation or
application of other statutes (this is done by reference
to avoid the need to set their provisions out at length).

22. Part II empowers the promoter to carry out the
requisite works, to deviate from the alignments specified,
to stop up highways and footpaths, to attach overhead
equipment to buildings, to underpin buildings. It also
gives details of the gauge and motive power and imposes
safeguards with regard to the use of electric power.
Part III is devoted to the acquisition of property rights
and the payment of compensation for their acquisition.
Part IV is concerned with the special interests of the
Crown, public utilities and highway authorities. Part V
sweeps up miscellaneous items: level crossings; power to
lop trees; power to make byelaws; power to levy fares;
rating; leases; planning; and arbitration. More
detailed provisions, especially as to the works (described
in words and by reference to the deposited plans) and the
lands to be acquired are set out in the Schedules. This
then in outline comprises the form and content of a
typical private tramways Act.

23. I have probably said enough to demonstrate that the
present arrangements for conferring authority on the
construction and operation of tramways are less than
ideal. The only practicable procedure is by way of the
private Bill and that is long, complex and expensive.
Other countries have simpler procedures. Why cannot this
be so here? It so happens that there has been
dissatisfaction with the private Bill procedure in several
other respects and this prompted the setting up of a Joint
Committee of the House of Lords and the House of Commons
to review the whole process to see whether changes might
be appropriate and whether resort to the procedure could
be avoided altogether in certain instances. The Committee
reported in July 1988.

24. As I have explained, the Committee were concerned
with private legislation in general, but several
recommendations were directed towards tramways. In
particular, the Committee observed:

> "that the Tramways Act needs considerable up-dating
> and revision to meet modern requirements, and that

there is no more need in principle for Parliament to
be concerned with trams than it is with lorries.
They recommend that a revised order-making procedure
for trams ... should be established by means of
primary legislation. They recommend that this
should be done quickly".

25. The suggested Order-making procedure would permit
tramway construction works and operation to be authorised
simply by the Secretary of State for Transport making an
Order. This Order would be prepared by the promoter,
would indicate the nature of the works and their location,
and include any requirements for compulsory purchase. The
draft Order would be advertised in each locality affected
and individual landowners would be directly notified.
There would be requirements to consult relevant Government
Departments, local authorities and public utility
undertakings. The Order could also grant planning
permission, but if this were done it would have to be made
jointly with the Secretary of State responsible for
planning matters.

26. If objection were to be made to a draft Order by a
person possessing the necessary locus, the Order could be
made only after the holding of a local public inquiry.
There would then be power for the Order to be amended or
rejected in the light of the inquiry recommendations.
Once made, the Order would have the same effect as an Act
of Parliament. The Tramways Act and the Light Railways
Acts would be repealed and resort to the private Bill
procedure would be greatly curtailed since it would not be
possible to invoke it unless it could be shown that it was
inappropriate to use the Order-making procedure.

27. Confronted with the prospect of a new regime which
would sweep away the complicated and archaic procedures
currently appertaining, would-be promoters might well be
expected to offer their enthusiastic support to the early
implementation of these recommendations. But there are
perhaps considerations which might give them grounds for
pause. The more obvious include: the enhanced role which
would be accorded to Government, already substantial in
the financial field; the presumed absence of anything
equivalent to the measured timetable which governs the
passage of a Bill; the planning aspects, which could give
rise to lengthy and expensive inquiries; and the fact
that the procedure would more easily be open to challenge
in the courts at the hands of determined objectors.

28. Early implementation of the proposals is therefore
a question not without important implications for light
rail schemes. The proposals have been debated in both

Houses and the reaction of the Government to them has been
guarded. While praising the Joint Committee for their
labours, they have placed much emphasis on the "tried and
tested" way in which rail schemes are currently handled
and they have stressed the need for more consultation.
There is no certainty therefore that the recommendations
will be adopted in the foreseeable future, although
measures such as those concerned with the Channel Tunnel
express rail link into central London are likely to keep
private Bill issues alive. There is the prospect
therefore of interesting developments ahead for tramways
and light rail systems in this sphere no less than in
others during the next few years.

14. Safety requirements for light rail

C. B. HOLDEN, BSc (Eng), FIRSE, Inspecting Officer of Railways, Department of Transport

SYNOPSIS. The Railway Inspectorate is responsible for advising the Secretary of State for Transport whether or not a new LRT system is safe to be opened to the public for the carriage of passengers. To gain approval for opening, a system will have to be inspected against a set of standards. These are in course of preparation by the Railway Inspectorate and the paper describes the current situation, summarises the recently issued Provisional Guidance Note on street-running, and foreshadows the likely contents of the Department of Transport's Requirements for LRT Systems.

BACKGROUND

1. The Railway Inspectorate was founded, in 1840, to provide advice to the Board of Trade, as to whether or not a railway was fit to be opened for the carriage of passengers. The advice given followed a thorough inspection of all the arrangements by an Inspector who was specifically and individually appointed for each task. Later the Inspectorate acquired the duty of accident investigation; this was formalised by an Act of Parliament in 1871. This 'interference' by national government with the workings of private individuals and Companies was anathema to many Victorians. However, a series of accidents and disasters and the deliberarations of a number of Royal Commissions led to the establishment of three principles, which, although eroded somewhat by more recent legislation, guide the work of the Inspectorate to this day.

2. These 'Victorian' principles can be summarised thus:

(a)   Once a railway is opened the state holds the Company responsible for maintaining it to the standard required for public safety.

(b)   The responsibility for the safe operation of a railway rests with the railway management.

(c)   Railway management must retain the responsibility

for the safe design of railway structures.

However, for the purposes of this paper, the first and the third principles are the ones which have the most effect. The first not only implies that the standards required for the final inspection have to be set and met but also these standards are the guide for the future operation of the railway. The third principle, which was established following the Tay Bridge Disaster in 1879, must nowadays be extended in its scope and, it is suggested, should be expressed as "Railway management must retain the responsibility for the safe design of all equipment, fixed or moving, where even oft-repeated testing may not or cannot, within an acceptable time-frame, reveal all hidden faults".

3. The standards required by the early Inspecting Officers of Railways were not codified until 1858 at which time they could easily be accommodated on one page of foolscap. Since then the Department's Railway Construction and Operation Requirements (ref.1) to give them their current full title but generally abbreviated to "The Requirements" or "The Blue Book", have steadily increased in size and scope. They have nevertheless remained non-mandatory in the strictly legal sense, thus allowing considerable flexibility in their application whilst retaining their essential function as a guide to the best and acceptable practice. It is essential to grasp this point which is in stark contrast to the situation which pertains to the highway.

4. Because meeting not only the Parliamentary procedures but also the Requirements for main line railways were inhibiting the growth of rail transport systems which fell outside the scope of the Tramways Act 1870 a different procedure yet again was devised under The Light Railways Act of 1896. The various governmental responsibilities under both these Acts were eventually passed to the Railway Inspectorate. The early requirements for tramways were either directly enacted in the Tramways Act itself or were included, as required by the Standing Orders of Parliament, in the Provisional orders which were granted under that Act and which were later confirmed as private Acts. The latest codification of standards to be met by tramways or street-running light railways is contained in the "1926 Memorandum" (ref.2). There is an equivalent document for trolley-buses.

5. As for railways, tramways also had to be inspected before being opened and this requirement has been carried on for the Light Rapid Transit (LRT) systems now being built or considered by ensuring that appropriate sections are

included in their enabling acts. However there were no modern standards which were appropriate to the types of system which were being contemplated. Much of the detailed technical impositions of the 1870 Tramways Act were far too out-of-date in the light of current technology as were the provisions of the 1926 Memorandum. Equally modern highway and road traffic legislation has omitted the references to tramways contained in their earlier counterparts with mixed effects, some advantageous, but in many instances leaving a statutory gap which will have to be filled.

THE CHALLENGE

6. The challenge which faced the Railway Inspectorate was therefore to produce a set of appropriate, modern standards for the UK where street-running rail vehicles had almost disappeared, with one, perhaps two, notable exceptions. It was thought some four years ago that this could be met by including a short section in the Requirements, which were at that time being revised. This short section, was, in essence, an updated version of the 1926 Memorandum and dealt almost exclusively with the railway-like aspects of modern trams. A draft of this revision was circulated for comment but drew surprisingly little response. Maybe it was too soon for those who are now actively promoting LRT systems and who are now beginning to ask for guidance on what will or will not be permitted. It also became apparent in late 1987 during discussions on Manchester's Metrolink that there was a need to re-educate highway and traffic engineers in how to incorporate an LRT system into the street-scene.

7. There were two other very different challenges. The first is not really germane to the main part of this paper but needs to be mentioned here to be picked up again later. It is that the political climate has led to the adoption of contractual arrangements which upset the traditional approach of approving-in-principle plans and equipment followed by continuous informed dialogue between the builder of the system, who was also the promoter, so that on final inspection there was little chance of there being something seriously wrong which would preclude the system from being opened to traffic. The second challenge stems from the very different philosophies adopted by the 'road' engineers from that used by the Railway Inspectorate in its approval procedure; to adopt a legal analogy the Inspectorate uses "case law" whereas in the case of roads decisions are based on a "Napoleonic Code". In other words, almost every aspect of road engineering, including the vehicles, is precisely laid down in a standard or in legislation therefore approval for general use follows automatically once it can be shown that that standard has been met, for example, by a specimen submitted for testing. This is in contrast to railway

practice where each aspect is inspected and approved on each occasion to determine its suitability for use; that determination being based, where appropriate, on precedent established in the light of guidelines contained in the Requirements. It will be appreciated that the foregoing are gross generalisations but it will help to explain why it has been necessary to achieve a modus vivendi by both disciplines concerned with LRT systems.

THE RESPONSE

8. As has been described the first response to these challenges was to set about drafting an appropriate section for The Requirements. During the discussions on Metrolink it became obvious that, although the outlines of a much-enlarged section, based on the original first draft, had been produced, the need was for a document which addressed much more directly the problems which were associated with the re-introduction into the street-scene of rail-borne vehicles; vehicles which were to be vastly different, not just in increased size, from those which had effectively disappeared from streets some thirty years ago. Accordingly work on The Requirements was suspended and a small working group was set up, led by the Inspectorate and supplemented when required by other members both within and from outside the Department of Transport. The result of this work was a provisional guidance note on the highway and vehicle engineering aspects of street-running light rapid transit systems (ref.3); known as the PGN for short.

9. At the same time as work was being done on the PGN it was realised that there were many matters which were not directly of an engineering nature which had to be addressed, only some of which had safety implications. It was therefore suggested to another division within the Department (Public Transport, Metropolitan) that they should set up a parallel working group. The two groups maintained close contact with each other by having an inner core of common membership. Whilst the second group has identified most of the issues with which it will need to deal and has decided what needs to be done, much of it requires change in the law and it is unlikely that these changes can be effected by the time Metrolink is due to open. However, the necessary advice will be available in good time and interim arrangements made.

THE PROVISIONAL GUIDANCE NOTE

10. In the following section of this paper some of the salient subjects covered in the PGN are summarised. Two points however need first to be made. It must be appreciated that the Note was principally directed towards highway and road traffic engineers and planners. Hence it contains only

a brief summary of the various features which will be required in the vehicles. Secondly the paragraphs which follow are a very selective and compressed summary of the detail, particularly of the traffic control systems, contained in the PGN.

11. For convenience, the following descriptions or definitions have been used throughout this paper:

(a)   Light Rapid Transit (LRT) Any guided transit system used for the carriage of passengers where the characteristics of the vehicles do not conform to those required for main line railways.

(b)   LRV The vehicle used on an LRT system.

(c)   LRT 1 The whole or part of an LRT system which runs in a road where the part of the carriageway used by the LRV is shared with other road users, including pedestrians.

(d)   LRT 2 The whole or part of an LRT system which runs in a road but where the LRT track is not shared, but is made accessible throughout its length for use by other road vehicles during traffic emergencies.

(e)   LRT 3 The whole or part of an LRT system where the LRT tracks are wholly segregated from other road traffic, including pedestrians, either within the boundaries of a highway or in a totally separate alignment. This category may be sub-divided into systems in which LRVs are operated:

> (i)   LRT 3a, on line of sight and will not require to be fully fenced;
>
> (ii)   LRT 3b, under the control of an interlocked signalling system and will normally be fully fenced.

(f)   Kinematic Envelope (KE) The full definition of the kinematic envelope is given in the Requirements. Briefly, it is the line around the track in a plane normal to the track which encloses the extreme position of the vehicle, and, where applicable, its load, under all conditions of its movement, when either stationary or moving along straight and level track, due to suspension movement, wear, tolerances in manufacture and the effects of tolerances in line, level and gauge of the track. By agreement, the effects of track tolerances may be separately allowed for. The KE is speed dependent.

(g)   Developed Kinematic Envelope (DKE) The developed

kinematic envelope is the KE enlarged to take into account all the possible effects of curvature, including superelevation of the track and end and centre throw of the vehicle. It, too, is speed dependent but is unique to the particular location at a given speed.

(h) The Swept Path The swept path is the DKE enlarged to take account of the required clearance outside the LRT track or tracks.

At-Grade Intersections

12. At-grade intersections over the LRT track are grouped into two main categories; those used by other road vehicles and those used by pedestrians. Combined pedestrian and other road vehicle crossings of the LRT system follow the principles laid down for each individual type according to the circumstances. The fundamental principle to be observed for each intersection is to use the minimum equipment possible consistent with providing adequate warning for all road users, including the mobility, visually and audibly impaired.

13. At-grade intersections of LRT 3b should be treated as level crossings would be on mainline railways and the LRV given absolute priority; those on LRT 3a as if they were intersections between major and minor roads and traffic signs and signals installed where necessary. At-grade intersections on LRT 1 and LRT 2 are treated as normal road layouts and the degree of precedence afforded to the LRV agreed with the Highway Authority.

Pedestrian Crossings with Signals

14. Where the crossing of the LRT tracks can be made entirely self-contained and a pedestrian can use it without needing to look out for other road traffic, the pedestrian crossing is "negatively" signalled; i.e. no warning (sound or signal), no LRV. However, if the LRT crossing cannot be in any way separated from the crossing of the remainder of the highway then a positive signal must be displayed whenever it is safe to cross. Such crossings, for example, would be at a traffic signalled road junction with a pedestrian phase or at a 'Pelican' crossing.

Traffic Signs

15. A range of road traffic signs, either entirely new or adaptations of existing signs, are shown. Equally, a set of signs for observance exclusively by LRV drivers has also been designed. Because it is not intended initially to include them in the current revision of the Traffic Signs

Regulations but to use them on a trial basis for the first one or two LRT systems to be built, all these signs will have to be specially authorised.

Traffic Signals

16. After much discussion, it has been decided that, firstly, special LRT traffic signals must be used and that ordinary red, amber, green signals should not. Secondly, two forms of the LRT signal head have been proposed, again with the intention of gaining some field experience in the UK before coming to a positive conclusion. The first form of the signal is for a single 300 mm diameter head containing a "multilamp" array where each of the aspects can be formed of a specified minimum number of lights out of a 5-light bar or central cluster. The central cluster can be flashed to give the equivalent of the flashing amber at a 'Pelican' crossing. Alternatively, three 200 mm diameter signal heads can be used which show similar aspects to those generated by the "21-eye" as it is at present colloquially known. A fibre-optic version of the 21-eye has also been tested.

17. Another decision arrived at after lengthy discussion was that the indication of the lie of a set of points should not be shown in the LRV traffic signal aspect but a separate points indicator signal was necessary. A possible form of that indicator, again a "multilamp" display and available off-the-shelf from some manufacturers, is illustrated in the PGN.

18. The control philosophy for LRT signals is that where they are associated with ordinary road traffic signals, they should be controlled by that local road traffic signal controller. Any route information generated by the LRT system must be presented locally to that controller through an LRT interface. All controllers and LRT interfaces must be designed to operate on their own even if the links to any supervisory systems fail. It is accepted that the fundamental system could be developed to encompass higher order traffic control systems.

19. The control system must be designed so that intersections can be safely controlled allowing such precedence for LRVs as may be agreed with the Highway Authority. In fixed time systems, the LRT stages will run irrespective of the presence of an LRV but in demand dependent systems, LRT signal phases will normally run in conjunction with parallel and complementary phases for other road users. However, separate stages or phases will be needed for LRV movements which conflict with other traffic flows. Phases used for LRVs must end with parallel phases for other traffic and allowance made for a longer closing

down period in LRT phases to guard against an LRV
overrunning the stop line after the all-red stage has
terminated. On LRT 3b lines, arrangements must be made at
pedestrian crossings to prevent an LRT aspect reverting to
stop if an LRV is within its service braking distance of the
crossing.

20. Signals for movements in the 'wrong' direction in an
emergency or during roadworks are not normally necessary as
such movements on LRT 1 or 2 systems can be made under the
supervision of a 'policeman' or his equivalent. However,
reversal of direction at a terminal or turnback station
should only take place on segregated parts of the system.

Highway and Carriageway Matters

21. The concept of the Kinematic Envelope (KE) of a moving
vehicle has been extended in the PGN. Whereas the KE,
although speed dependent, takes no account of the effects of
curvature, a new parameter, called the developed Kinematic
envelope (DKE), does. The DKE is therefore also speed
dependent but is unique to a particular location at a given
vehicle speed. The DKE is further enlarged by the required
safety clearance outside the LRT track or tracks to give the
Swept Path. The Swept Path should in principle be marked and
the use of different colour or texture where traffic lanes
are shared is suggested. The adequate marking of the Swept
Path is particularly critical in pedestrian zones. The
clearance between the DKEs must be at least 380 mm where two
LRT lanes abut, but the edge of the Swept Path is at least
280 mm outside the DKE. Based on an LRV having a nominal
width of 2650 mm, lanes shared with other traffic on a
single carriageway should not normally be less than 3530 mm
wide. However, where there are two or more lanes in a single
direction and the LRT lane is shared with HGVs or PSVs, the
minimum width is 3300 mm but the preferred lane width is
3650 mm. Ideally, adjacent lanes for other traffic should be
wider than that but should never be less than 3250 mm wide.
Illustrations showing the application of these clearances to
various layouts, including a pedestrian precinct, are at
figures 1 to 3.

22. More agressive methods than plain lining must be used to
define the reserved track for LRT 2 as shown in figure 4.
However, it is recognised that emergency service vehicles
and buses substituting for LRVs during emergency working
must have convenient accesses to and from the reserved track
which should normally be about 150 mm above the remainder of
the carriageway level. Access by other than LRVs to the
segregated tracks of an LRT 3 system must be barred by
traffic signs and suitable treatment of the road surface
leading to them.

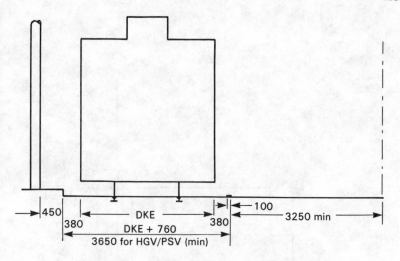

SHARED LANE — GUTTER RUNNING

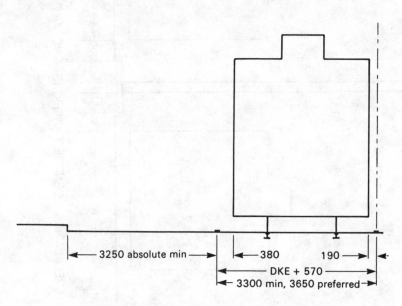

SHARED LANE — CENTRE RUNNING

FIGURE 1

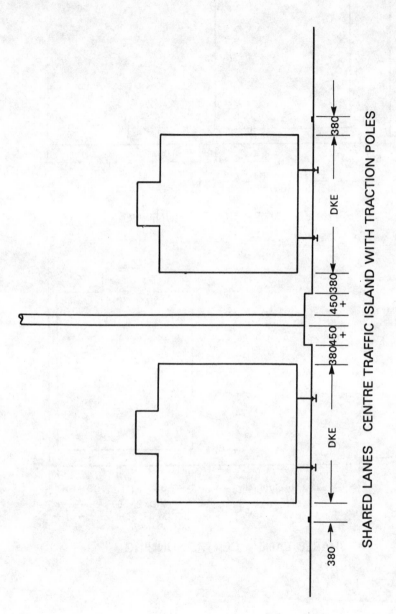

SHARED LANES   CENTRE TRAFFIC ISLAND WITH TRACTION POLES

FIGURE 2

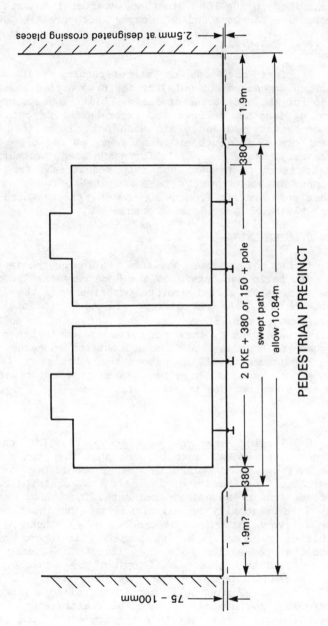

PEDESTRIAN PRECINCT

FIGURE 3

211

23. The needs of cyclists and of frontagers (people with property adjacent to the kerb) are assessed and measures prescribed in the PGN. Other measures dealing with fencing, protective barriers and deflecting kerbs are also described.

Stations and Stops

24. Stations or stops on street-running systems form a particular hazard not only for the prospective passenger but also for the pedestrian at large. Whilst there seems to be a growing tendency to have low floor-height or even very low floor-height vehicles, this does not change the fact that some form of platform and a safe way on and off it will be necessary. Where higher platforms are used, precautions need to be taken to prevent not only pedestrians from becoming trapped between them by on-coming LRVs, but also to stop other road traffic from using the LRT tracks where two such high platforms are opposite each other.

THE REQUIREMENTS

25. It has not yet been possible, following the issue of the PGN, to begin work again on the Requirements. The following few paragraphs will therefore describe more the intentions rather than the actuality of the contents of the Requirements for LRT systems. This, however, is no bad thing as, in some senses, they can serve as one of the discussion documents. Because the PGN also contains an earnest of what the Requirements will say about the vehicles or LRVs and a number of decisions have been taken about Metrolink's LRVs it seems appropriate to start with them.

LRVS

26. <u>End-loading strengths and couplers</u>. The end-loading strengths of an LRV must be such that they can accommodate the buffing and drawgear loads. They should provide adequate protection for the driver in a serious collision but resist deformation in 'shunting' accidents. They should conform to any internationally agreed standards. They must be uniform for all vehicles using the system, except those maintenance vehicles used only during non-traffic hours or during absolute possession of the line. The loads may be distributed throughout the length of the vehicle. For road safety reasons couplers for LRVs on systems which include LRT 1 and LRT 2 must be protected by suitable fendering and preferably not protrude beyond the vehicle ends when not in use. It is apparent that this requirement is not easily met by existing designs of automatic coupler. The conflicting interests of road safety, operating convenience and sound, practical design will therefore need to be resolved.

27. <u>Fendering</u>.   The requirement to have a drop-down
life-guard tray has been changed from compulsory to
optional. However the body of the LRV must be fitted with
skirts to prevent, as far as is reasonably practicable,
access to the underside of the LRV.   These skirts must be
arranged to push away from the path of the vehicle anything
which may come into inadvertent contact with the LRV. The
sides of the vehicle as well as its ends must be fendered
unless its construction is such as to prevent underrunning
in the event of a collision with another road vehicle.

28. <u>Body - Construction.</u> The LRV must be designed to meet
requirements of BS 6853: Code of Practice for Fire
Precautions in the Design and Construction of Railway
Passenger Rolling Stock. However it will be necessary for
the vehicle to meet the Category I standard wherever the LRV
is required to use a single-track, single-bore tunnel or
there are significant lengths where the line is carried on
structures with limited access to the track. Any forward
facing window must be of high-impact resistant glass; side
windows should conform to current PSV standards. However,
windows in the passenger compartment must, if they open, be
of the inward-opening hopper type. Similarly, windows in the
driving cab should preferably be non-opening but in any
event must not open in such a manner that the driver can
extend any part of his head or body beyond the kinematic
envelope unless full clearances exist throughout the system.

29. <u>Body - Interior.</u> Fittings must be designed to that
they, as far as possible, will not cause secondary injuries
to passengers should the LRV be involved in an accident.
Where the vehicles are designed to accommodate standing
passengers adequate grab rails must be provided. In any
event, provision must be made for the carriage of the
mobility impaired, especially those in wheelchairs. An
appropriate fire extinguisher must be readily accessible to
the driver and other emergency equipment, including ladders
where necessary, carried in marked lockers.

30. <u>Doors and Steps</u>.   Ideally the LRV floor should be at
the same height above the rails as the platform. Where this
is impracticable it must be possible to achieve a level
transfer through at least one door, which must be adjacent
to the space allotted for wheel-chairs. If folding steps or
sliding plates are necessary where the maximum stepping
distance from platform to LRV floor would otherwise be
exceeded these must be interlocked with the traction power
controller, either directly or through the door mechanism.
The doors themselves must be designed to detect the presence
of obstructions and must be interlocked with the traction
controller so that power cannot be taken unless all the
doors are fully closed and is cut off should any door be
opened.

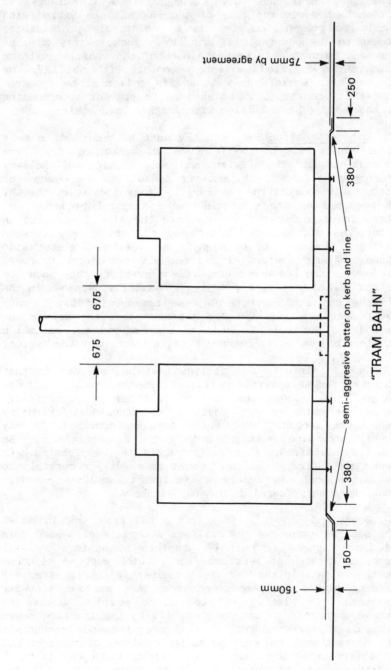

"TRAM BAHN"

FIGURE 4

31. Mirrors.   Rear-view mirrors are required for two purposes; for normal road traffic purposes and to enable the driver of a one-man operated LRV to check that nobody has been trapped by a closed door and is being dragged along by a moving vehicle. A somewhat larger mirror may be needed so that the driver can see when boarding or alighting has been completed. [For convenience the terms mirror and driver have been used to cover, in the first instance, any device which can give the requisite view and in the second any member of the LRV crew or LRT staff charged with the duty of checking that it is safe for an LRV to start from a station or stop]. Traditionally, mirrors have been folding and deployed only when at a stand because they obtruded from the bodysides of the vehicle. It is intended to stiffen this requirement so that the obligatory mirrors remain within the KE; the larger optional mirror must therefore retract or fold and be interlocked in a similar way to the doors and steps.

32. Lights and Horns. The Road Vehicle Lighting Regulations 1989 came into force on 1 November 1989. They do not cover LRVs. However it is felt that wherever possible the spirit of these regulations should be observed for LRVs on LRT 1 and LRT 2 systems. Hence front and rear position lamps, end outline marker lamps, brake lights, headlamps and direction indicators will be required but some relaxation for them not being more than 400 mm from the bodysides will probably be necessary. Similarly relaxation will be needed for the permissible heights above ground. Side marker lights are not required for passenger vehicles under the regulations but it is considered that these should be fitted to LRVs. Their maximum distance from the end of the LRV and their pitch may have to depend on the door spacings but at present 3 metres (or 4m if 3m is not possible) is the value being considered. These lamps will be amber and again, at present, it is thought that they will be combined with the side-mounted direction indicators so that they will flash off coincidentally with the front and rear direction indicators. There are two distinct requirements for headlamps; for street running they must show a distinctive LRV pattern but for use on LRT 3 sections a high intensity light must be shown at all times to warn staff at work on or about the track of the approach of an LRV. The first requirement will probably be met by having, in addition to the pair of dipped headlights described in the lighting regulations, a third lamp mounted centrally above (or exceptionally below) the line of the other two lamps. This third lamp should be switchable so that when running on the streets when the other lamps are lit then only the dipped beam is available but when on LRT 3 parts of a system and the other lamps are extinguished the high-intensity, long-range beam is shown. For the same reasons as for headlamps two forms of audible warning will probably be necessary; on the street sections a

distinctive LRV sound and on LRT 3 sections a somewhat louder, more penetrating sound. Tram buffs hanker after the bell for the former but an A4 chime-whistle has also been suggested!

33. Electrical Systems. Except on totally segregated i.e. LRT 3 systems, overhead current collection will be required, the main traction-power circuit breaker must be roof-mounted and an isolating switch readily available to the LRV driver. Other electrical circuits should also be protected by switches and circuit breakers. Metal parts of the LRV body must be connected to the negative return. Traction power cables must be routed so that in a road-traffic accident they are, as far as possible, protected from mechanical damage. However, cubicles containing equipment at traction supply voltage should be accessible only from outside the passenger compartment. Any which have to be in the driver's compartment must be locked shut by a high-security lock and warning notices posted. Cubicles containing power control equipment which could emit toxic fumes if set on fire must not be ventilated into the passenger compartment. A combined traction-power and brake controller is preferred.

34. Brakes. Whilst it is comparatively easy to set down the principles of the braking systems needed for LRVs it has proved more controversial to define the precise performance requirements; the PGN carefully avoided giving exact rates. A continuous electric or pneumatic 'fail-safe' brake must be fitted to operate on all cars of a coupled train. Every independent vehicle must have a parking brake. This can be mechanical or spring-applied, power held-off. Where the required performance cannot be achieved by brakes operating through the running wheels then additional brakes operating directly on the track and independent of the traction power supply are required. The normal braking system should achieve a braking rate of 1.3m/s^2 under emergency conditions and a track-brake about 3.0m/s^2. However the parking brake must be able to hold a loaded LRV on the steepest slope. There is a danger to passengers if too severe a brake is used so the application of the brakes must not impose a jerk-rate which would endanger standing passengers at whatever speed the LRV may be travelling; this is not likely to be above 0.8m/s^3 with an absolute maximum of 1m/s^3.

Traction Power Supplies

35. The electric traction power will normally be supplied from an overhead line system at a voltage not exceeding 750v DC nominal for LRT 1 and LRT 2 systems. This may be increased to 1500v DC for LRT 3. Systems which are wholly LRT 3 may exceptionally use a conductor rail power supply

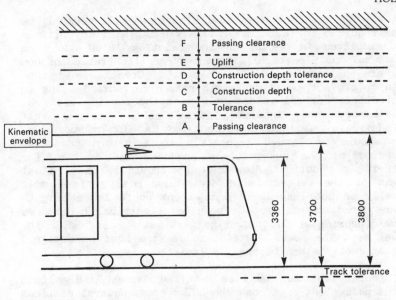

Dimensions (mm)		Without supports	With supports		Special reduced clearance
			Preferred	Reduced tolerance	
F	Passing clearance, OHLE to structure	200	100	100	
E	Uplift	70	70	70	
D	Construction depth tolerance	75	75	10	
C	Constuction depth	120	120	120	See note.
B	Passing clearance tolerance	75	75	10	
A	Passing clearance	100	100	100	
	Kinematic envelope – typical	3800	3800	3800	
	Track tolerance	25	25	15	
Height of structure above designed rail level	At supports		4365	4225	
	Between Supports	4465			
Designed height of OHLE wire above designed rail level		4000	4000	3920	

Dimensional constraints on vehicle, structures and
overhead line equipment (OHLE)

Note Lower clearances may be permitted in certain
circumstances at the discretion of the Department
of Transport's Railway Inspectorate.

FIGURE 5

system. The required electrical clearances will normally be those required for mainline railways using similar voltages and are given in detail in the existing 'Blue Book' on Structural and Electrical Clearances. An illustration of how they are applied is given in figure 5. Great care must be taken to prevent any stray earth-return currents leading to electrolitic corrosion. Not only must the running rails be cross-bonded and insulated from earth but a half Farraday-cage below the permanent way is also recommended. This should be bonded separately to a return conductor connected to the sub-station. Adequate test points for measuring the current flow must be provided. The nominal height of the contact wire above the road surface must normally be not less than 5.5m except where lower heights are required to achieve the required electrical clearances below overbridges. Such lower heights must be signed in the normal way. The power distribution system must be designed so that sections can be readily isolated.

36. Special treatment will be required where DTp High Load Routes pass along or across the LRT system. Neutral sections will be needed and arrangements made for raising or removing the overhead wiring. Span-wires suspended from poles or from rosettes on buildings or, alternatively, stanchions with cantilevers may be used to support the overhead contact wire. If the span-wire poles are used to carry street-lighting or other electrified equipment such as illuminated traffic signs then they must be double insulated. Such poles should be located at least 460 mm clear of the carriageway. The arrangements for earthing or bonding stanchions or poles will depend on the complete arrangements for the minimisation of stray, earth-return, traction current. These must also take into account the need to keep the touch-potential of the pole above the local earth potential to the minimum. Guard wires may be needed to prevent other overhead cables from touching those of the LRT system and other defences provided to prevent deliberate climbing of the poles or accidental touching of the live equipment. Similarly, defences will be needed to guard against the deliberate fouling of the live equipment where it passes beneath an overbridge; standards similar to those for main line railways will be applicable.

Signalling and Communication

37. The object of any signalling system is to prevent collisions and derailments on points. The system of signalling on street-running sections has been described already. On LRT 3 stretches line of sight signalling is perfectly admissible. However, on former railway alignments experience has shown that for the line speeds desired it is

not often that sufficient sighting distance is available. The ability of an LRV driver to estimate the range and closing speed to a preceding LRV, particularly at night, also has to be addresssed when considering whether or not to use any form of signalling system. The 'Signals' themselves do not have to be the main line railway standards. Because the meaning of the proceed aspect probably differs from that on the street the use of the "21-eye" in a larger version, which was at one time considered, may not be appropriate. Where an LRT system runs alongside a main line railway, similar looking signals would have to be co-located to prevent misreading. Therefore, if the signal spacing for each system is very different, lineside signals may not be appropriate for the LRT system. If cab signalling is used lineside markers to indicate where such signals should be received will be necessary. If a form of Automatic Train Control is fitted then Automatic Train Protection must form part of it. For all forms of signalling, including line of sight, the normal 'service' braking rate, about 1.3 m/s^3, should be used to determine the spacing. However, if a form of caution is used to supplement line of sight signalling then the use of emergency braking rates may be admissible.

38. It is particularly critical on street sections to avoid trapping anything, such as the heel of a shoe, in a moving point. Probably the best way of doing this is to delay setting the route until the LRV is sufficiently close so as to act as a deterrent in itself. However it must be possible for the LRV to be stopped short of the points should they fail to set properly. Hence the route calling device must be located some distance before the place where the driver must respond to the points-set signal. The necessary calculations are illustrated in figure 6. Whatever arrangements are made for route calling, either on or off street, these must ensure that the route is held whilst an LRV is approaching and traversing points. If track-circuits are used these must, of course, be immunised against traction or traction-induced currents. The need for a proper interface between the LRT system and the traffic signal controllers is described in detail in the PGN. Where each 'end' of an LRV is separately identified, for route calling and releasing, then arrangements must be made to inhibit the 'middle' where two or more LRVs are coupled together.

39. There is no intrinsic objection to using radio for safety signalling purposes. However, such radio must be selective in that, except for 'emergency' transmissions, only the vehicle being addressed should receive an 'action' message either as data or as a voice transmission. Open channel radio is suitable only for advisory purposes. LRVs should normally be fitted with a driver-to-passenger PA

THE CASE OF THE STILLETTO HEEL or THE ROVER'S PAW PROBLEM

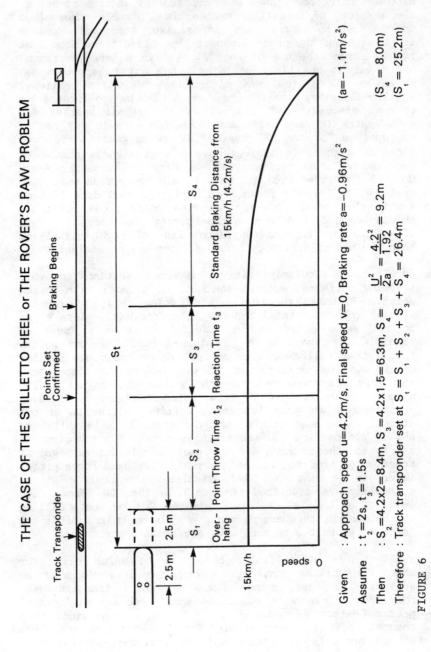

Given : Approach speed u=4.2m/s, Final speed v=0, Braking rate a=−0.96m/s² (a=−1.1m/s²)

Assume : $t_2 = 2s$, $t_3 = 1.5s$

Then : $S_2 = 4.2 \times 2 = 8.4m$, $S_3 = 4.2 \times 1.5 = 6.3m$, $S_4 = -\dfrac{U^2}{2a} = \dfrac{4.2^2}{1.92} = 9.2m$ (S_4 = 8.0m)

Therefore : Track transponder set at $S_t = S_1 + S_2 + S_3 + S_4 = 26.4m$ (S_t = 25.2m)

FIGURE 6

system and, where single-manned vehicles are routed through single-bore tunnels, this system must, if the driver becomes incapacitated, be accessible by central control through the LRV radio.

Way and Works

40. Definitions of KE etc. have been given earlier as have the clearances between the KE and other KEs of carriageway lanes. On LRT3 sections the clearances to structures will be as for mainline railways except that, where non-opening or inward opening hopper windows are provided, then the clearance to a structure may be reduced to 75 mm. However safe walkways for staff must be provided on at least one side of the formation. These clearances are illustrated in figure 7. The treatment of clearances at platform edges will need to be discussed with the Railway Inspectorate because there will almost certainly be a conflict between the normal clearances and the requirement to have an LRV as close to the platform edge as possible, at least over the portion designated for use by the mobility impaired. Such treatments are illustrated in figure 8.

41. Most of the requirements for mainline railways in respect of the formation, alignment and structures generally will also apply to LRT systems but with allowances for obvious differences say as between steel-wheel on steel-rail systems and rubber-wheel on concrete beam-systems. However, the minimum radius of curvature will normally be 18m on standard gauge track and 12m on metre gauge. The maximum gradient should not normally be steeper than 5% but, provided that the braking system on the LRV is suitable and the Inspectorate agrees, this may be increased to 12%.

42. A careful choice of tyre and rail profile is needed to reduce noise and other vibrations. Flangeways should be kept to the minimum so as to avoid causing a nuisance to other road users. The requirements for turnouts on street-sections are discussed in the PGN.

43. The treatment of stations on LRT3 must follow the principles set out in the Requirements for mainline railways. However, there is one important proviso. Where the LRT system uses low platforms and is adjacent on the same formation to a main line without a station then the two systems must have a fence between them, extending for at least 100m from either end of the LRT station. This is to prevent passengers, who may legitimately cross the LRT tracks, from doing the same on the main line.

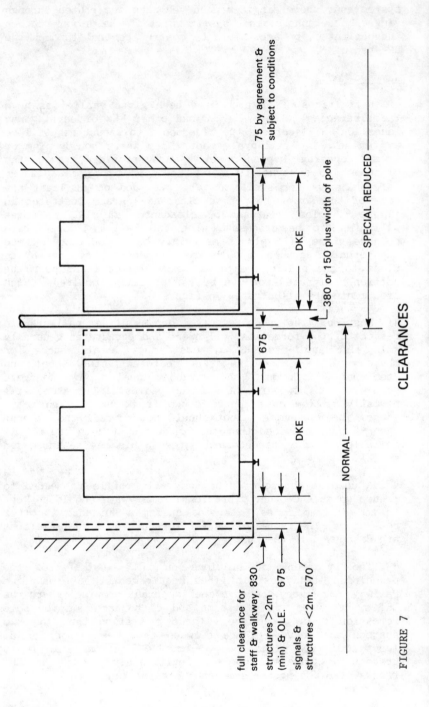

FIGURE 7

CLEARANCES

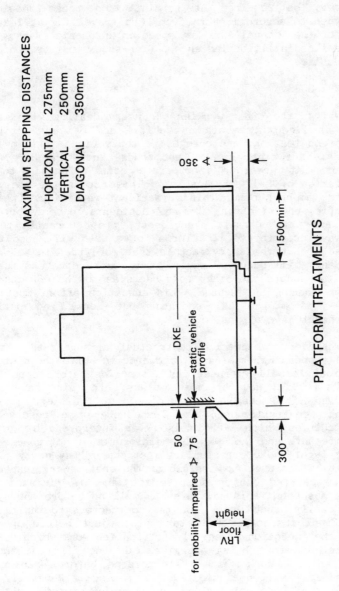

MAXIMUM STEPPING DISTANCES

HORIZONTAL 275mm
VERTICAL   250mm
DIAGONAL   350mm

PLATFORM TREATMENTS

FIGURE 8

223

44. Generally speaking the requirements for protection against trespass are much less onerous on LRT systems than on the main line; with the one exception being those automatically driven LRT 3b systems. Buffer-stops will, however, be required at terminii and these should be designed to absorb impacts from LRVs travelling at least 15 km/h or the 'manual' driving speed on automatic systems. The space immediately behind such buffer-stops must be denied to the public.

OTHER ISSUES

45. Whilst the other working party are dealing with issues such as licensing (both of vehicle and driver), drivers' hours and testing, and changes to the various traffic laws, there is one other aspect that needs mentioning here. Most systems, at present, incorporate some reference to the Regulation of Railways Act 1871. This Act is the one which covers, amongst other things, accident reporting. It makes specific provision for 'tramway' accidents to be reported in the same way as railway accidents, i.e. currently to the Railway Inspectorate. The forms to be used will need to be looked at but the sorry fact is that road traffic and other accidents will occur. However, much can be done and must be done to educate the other road users as to the effects of a street-running LRT system. This education effort must come largely from the LRT operator but local and national Government have a part to play.

46. Whatever the precise contractual arrangements, it is, legally speaking, the party empowered to build the system who must formally request its inspection before opening it to the public. However, since plans, etc. also have to be approved, it seems sensible to set up a dialogue between client, contractor and the Inspectorate to resolve any difficulties which might arise over interpretation of the Requirements and the PGN. This dialogue must not obscure the exact legal and contractual obligations of any party. It is helpful if as much as possible of the preliminary inspection can be carried out as soon as the work is finished or a stage has been finished. This may well be before the system is formally handed over from the contractors to the client. The final inspection will take place just before opening, with the exception of any electrification work which must be inspected before being energised. On the final inspection any remedial work which must be done before opening (or energising) will be indicated and opening is generally made conditional upon correcting any other deficiencies within a given period of time.

47. Whilst some of the contents of this paper have been drawn from previously published material much of it is based on documents and policies which are still being finalised by the Railway Inspectorate and as such represent the author's own interpretation of what these may eventually be. Readers should note this disclaimer carefully and should check with the Inspectorate before committing themselves to a course of action based on the contents of this paper. The author is grateful to the Chief Inspecting Officer of Railways for permission to publish it and to his colleagues for their assistance in writing it.

REFERENCES

1. DEPARTMENT OF TRANSPORT. Railway Construction and Operation Requirements. HMSO 1950, 1977 (Structural and Electrical Clearances), 1981 and 1985 (Level Crossings)

2. MINISTRY OF TRANSPORT. Tramways and Light Railways laid on Public Roads; Memorandum regarding Details of Construction of New Lines and Equipment. Ministry of Transport 1926.

3. DEPARTMENT OF TRANSPORT. Provisional Guidance Note on the Highway and Vehicle Engineering Aspects of Street-Running Light Rapid Transit Systems. The Railway Inspectorate April 1989.

15. Commercial options and implementations

R. RICHARDSON and D. S. ASHBURNER, Trafalgar House

1. INTRODUCTION

Privately funded projects in transport infrastructure are experiencing a renaissance but our ideas on the forms of contract and associated risks are still developing. This paper discusses aspects of the Trafalgar House approach and comments on current and recent projects.

Any commuter travelling to work by train, car or bus in our big cities knows that there is a crisis in urban travel, overcrowding, and on some lines worn out rolling stock. Light Rail Transit Systems (LRTS) are viewed as one cost effective solution for the medium sized conurbation. In the post Victorian era transport infrastructure has been funded directly by government grant, but the present Government has a policy of reducing public expenditure by involving private sector finance.

The first of the public Light Rail projects with private sector support recently commenced in Manchester. Schemes are being considered in many other centres, particularly in West Midlands, Sheffield, Bristol, Leeds and Southampton.

In this paper I will sketch our approach to such projects.

2. OVERALL PROJECT MANAGEMENT

Trafalgar House aims to obtain the maximum long term sustainable return to its shareholders consistent with sound business principles. We embark on major projects only after a full assessment of the risks and rewards.

Project investment falls broadly into three categories:

1. Short term investment, for example the labour, plant and material costs to execute a particular project under various contractual conditions and on which we would expect to see a return by the time the contract was completed.

2. Medium term investment which may include land purchase subsequently destined for industrial, commercial or residential development.

3. (Of particular relevance to Light Rail Transit Systems), <u>Medium to long term</u> investment where Trafalgar House is both an equity investor in the project, as well as having group companies executing the construction contracts. Examples are the new Dartford Bridge and the proposed Indonesian Toll Road project where profits on the equity accrue late in the concession period.

Urban LRT systems, with a relatively definable market appear suitable for partial financing by industry in that concessions to operate can be valued.

There are of course more opportunities than we have resources to pursue so our appraisal procedure starts with a sieving process of the numerous ideas generated separating the wheat from the chaff to permit concentration on areas of particular expertise. Projects may be home grown, joint ventures and even occasionally those proposed by the enthusiastic amateur.

The initial short list is often arrived at by intuitive methods but the decision made to invest in and promote some rather than others is based on the following considerations:–

–   Does it fit the division's strategic plan?

–   What is the capital investment, period, rate and size of return?

–   Geographical location   – ie. does Trafalgar House operate in the area?
                             – potential for joint ventures

–   What is the general nature of the project; has a similar thing been achieved before?

–   Mode of financing

–   Political considerations.

–   Project risks, eg. design, construction, programme

–   Competition and up front investment.

TRAFALGAR HOUSE

Trafalgar House was founded in 1956, floated on the London Stock Exchange in 1963 and is now one of the UK's largest public companies, capitalised at around £2 billion.

The group has three business streams;

>   – Construction and Engineering
>   – Commercial and Residential Property
>   – Shipping and Leisure

Trafalgar House is;

One of the largest construction and related engineering groups in the UK

A leading property developer

The fifth largest house builder in the UK

Owner of the world's most famous passenger liner – The QE2

228

Second largest UK based container ship operator

40% shareholder in BREL Ltd.

Within the group there are over 150 operating companies, working in more than 80 countries directly employing more than 30,000 people.

Trafalgar House has succeeded in part due to the group's ability to see opportunities early, hopefully before our competition, and to bring the projects to fruition at a profit.

So what is our interest in LRTS which are medium rather than 'mega' in scale.

1. Trafalgar House has recently become a major player in transport. We acquired 40% share in BREL Ltd, formally British Rail Engineering Ltd, who have over 150 years expertise in the design, manufacturer and maintenance of vehicles and coaches.

    BREL is currently undertaking orders to a value exceeding £1 billion. These principally comprise:

    –   the largest order ever placed in the UK for urban tubestock – 680 rapid transit cars for London Underground Limited's Central Line renewal programme, deliveries of which are planned to begin in mid 1991;

    –   a succession of orders, totalling 447 cars, for Class 158 diesel multiple units for BRS's Provincial Express Services, deliveries of which will continue until late 1991;

    –   orders for 180 Class 165 diesel multiple units for BRB's Network SouthEast, which will be delivered through 1991;

    –   completion of an order for Mark IV passenger coach bodies and driving van trailers for BRB's West Coast Main Line services;

    –   a number of smaller new build orders for BRB (Classes 319 and 456 EMUs) and overseas (DMUs for Thailand);

    –   a wide range of coach, multiple unit and locomotive repairs and refurbishments for BRB, and, to a lesser extent, other customers in the UK and overseas; and

    –   a range of components and spares for BRB and other customers in the UK and overseas.

2. Trafalgar House was one of the first UK companies to promote a private infrastructure project. The Dartford bridge is on programme for operation in 1991. We have also been selected along with BICC to join with BR in the development of the Channel Tunnel rail link. Our housing and property companies are also available to advise our project teams on potential development gain. Although not directly relevant to transport schemes, Trafalgar House in involved in a number of schemes for privately funded power stations and tidal barrages. These involve similar risks. Thus LRTS offer opportunities both short term to several Trafalgar House companies and long term to our transport interests.

3.   Thirdly through our ownership of major construction companies such as Cementation, Trollope & Colls, Cleveland Bridge and Engineering, and John Brown, we have the engineering expertise to design, construct and procure the required infrastructure.

4.   We seek to make a profit. Few if any transport systems operate without subsidies of some sort. Many if not most LRTS in Europe do not make a profit and are subsidised.

3. PROJECT FINANCE

Whilst project finance is the subject of other papers, one or two comments may be appropriate.

Most of the proposed Light Rail Systems will serve a definable market, where the traffic and patronage income are to some extent predictable. Long concession periods are possible and at Dartford for example, a highly leveraged innovative financial package was designed where of the total £200m+ raised, only £1,000 was true equity. The remaining monies comprised long term bank loans, fixed rate loan stock, fixed rate subordinated loan stock, and uniquely to Dartford, toll revenue during construction A careful assessment of the project risks was required, and the lenders and investors (mainly insurance companies) were asked to accept new risks, eg. revenue and operation, with limited security.

The subordinated loan stock holders, mainly bid consortium members, in addition carried the residual risks, particularly those associated with design and construction. To reflect this a high fixed rate of return was required.

The Government will wish to minimise the public grant requirement, hence private tenderers will seek to reduce the capital costs whilst maximising the concession value. These two aims are interrelated and the development of the finance plan is an iterative process and requires close co-operation between the designer, contractor, forecaster, financier and owner.

4.   RISKS

I would now like to comment on possible forms of contract for light railway schemes and to illustrate these by referring briefly to a number of recent and current projects.

All of the LRT schemes under consideration present significant and possible large risks to the private company and in most cases potential profit whether from operating the system or from supplying the equipment and construction services, is likely to be relatively modest. In other words, major structural failure of a bridge or small errors in estimating the patronage, may wipe out the projected profit. I will comment on the following schemes; Manchester Metrolink, Midlands Metro, Sheffield Supertram, London Underground Jubilee Line, Channel Tunnel High Speed Link, Dartford Bridge, the Channel Tunnel and Tyne & Wear Metro.

1. **Manchester Metrolink**

Project Description

The GMPTE invited tender submissions for the design, construction, operation and maintenance of a Light Rail Transit System (LRTS) running from Altrincham through Manchester city centre to Bury. For the majority of its 30km length the system will use existing British Rail alignments, although a street running section is to connect Victoria and Piccadilly stations with the G Mex shopping and leisure centre. The city centre section is central for proposed extensions to Trafford Park, Salford Quays, Oldham and Rochdale.

The principle of the tender competition was that bidders were required to value a 15 year operating concession. This value would then be deducted from the capital cost in order to determine the magnitude of the public grant required. On completion of the concession period the LRT system would be returned to the GMPTE free of charge.

History

The Greater Manchester LRT project developed from initial studies and discussions carried out in 1981 and 1985, and in April 1988 the GMPTE announced its intention to proceed.

Tenders were invited for a design, build, operate and transfer package. The procedure was divided into three stages, prequalification, stage I and finally stage II. This in order to permit adequate competition and the development of proposals. A final bid date of May 1989 was specified. It was envisaged that up to eight consortia would compete within stage I reducing to between two and four for stage II.

Stage 1

Trafalgar House was one of eight prequalifiers selected for stage I.

The envisaged structure was similar to Dartford in that a concession company (GMRT Co) was to be formed which would then award design and construction, operation and maintenance contracts, retaining only the risks associated with patronage.

The concession value was assessed on the basis of the debt that could be raised on the projected cash flows (revenue – operating costs) and the equity that could be sustained by the cash flows once the debt had been serviced. The debt would be raised on a limited resource basis.

Annual revenue was determined from the patronage projections provided by the GMPTE, together with an allowance for vehicle advertising and franchise operations.

Stage 2

On 15 March 1989 Trafalgar House and the other consortia were invited to submit a stage II tender.

The initial intention was that this phase of the bid procedure would permit consolidation of the design and construction packages and discussion regarding the conditions of contract, forms of guarantee and various agreements in order to present committed unqualified bids by the revised tender date of 30 June.

Release of revised Stage II tender documentation was delayed until 6 June. Briefly, this required fixed and fluctuating prices with two guarantee options. The short bidding period, although extended until 25 July, combined with further releases of information, made the preparation of a fixed price offer impossible. The contract agreement and price structure were more onerous than at Stage I.

The overall contract structure envisaged the concession company placing separate contracts for operation, construction work and supply of rolling stock. The rolling stock in our case was to be supplied through the construction consortium but would be the property of the GMPTE. At the time of bidding two forms of guarantee were suggested by the client:

1. Joint and several, 100% performance and financial guaranty for 15 year concession period. Guaranty to cover all risks, apart from limited exceptions, extending to all obligations of GMRT Co. No facility to withdraw from the consortium.

2. As 1, however limited to construction and three year operation period. GMRT Co required to be fully capitalised and solvent on completion of the guaranty period. Solvency tests could be applied at any time during the guaranty. Financial guaranty applies to any latent defects and would continue if claims arose due to failure in initial three years. GMPTE retained various rights to terminate agreement with inadequate provision for compensation

In both cases the guarantors ranked behind the PTE in the insolvency of GMRT Co. The lending institutions would have no call on the assets of GMRT Co, ie rolling stock, cash flow and no right to restructure GMRT Co in cases of default.

Apart from the general severity of these guarantees, the principal risks were as follows:

1. Source data. The PTE supplied the basic data for the design and revenue calculations but refused to warrant this.

2. Part of the track proposed had been used by BR for many years but the structural state of bridges and embankments was uncertain and in the event of failure might have cost the concession company significant sums of money.

3. Third party consents, agreements and transfers. Some of these were plainly not within the control of the concession company or construction consortium.

4. PTE and their statutory rights of inspection.

5. Fare levels. Any increases required were subject to Section 6 of the Fair Trading Act.

6. Penalties for failure to meet service frequencies were proposed. This seemed to us unacceptable as loss of revenue should have been a sufficient penalty.

2. **Midlands Metro**

Midlands Metro is the scheme for connecting a number of towns in the Midlands from Coventry to Wolverhampton by a light railway system to be built in several phases.

Project Description

Royal Assent has been obtained for the first line running north west from Birmingham Snow Hill to Wolverhampton via West Bromwich and Bilston. The majority of the 21km route will be segregated off street, running along disused railway alignments. On entering Wolverhampton vehicles will transfer to on-street operation.

The initial service, serving 22 stations will require 20 vehicles running at 10 minute intervals, providing a capacity of 1,500 passengers per hour in each direction. The infrastructure will be designed to provide for increased frequency of 5 and 2 minutes. The capital cost is estimated at £65m.

A Parliamentary Bill has been submitted for two future lines. These are:

1. City centre underground to Aston University, continuing on to Birmingham Heartlands and the airport. Capital cost £240m, 26km route, 34 stations with 24 vehicles at 5 minute headway.

2. Wolverhampton to Dudley via Walsall. Capital cost £120m, 26km route, and 11 vehicles at 10 minute headway.

The Bill for a separate system in Coventry should be lodged by November 1991.

The form of contract preferred by the WMPTE is not yet known. Obviously the options include repeating the Manchester structure or having a Project Manager (a PMC in the offshore structural industry). Decisions on the form of contract are not entirely with the PTE in any of these cases. The Department of Transport may require a greater transfer of risk. Perhaps this could be a separate contract for operation.

3. **Sheffield Supertram**

At present our company is not significantly involved in the Sheffield scheme although BREL Ltd, in which we are a 40% shareholder, together with ABB, are tendering for the rolling stock and vehicle maintenance.

Project Description

The project involves the construction of a 22 km light railway linking Hillsborough in the North via the city centre with Mosborough in the South. A branch into the lower Don Valley is included. Parliamentary powers have been obtained. Approxi-

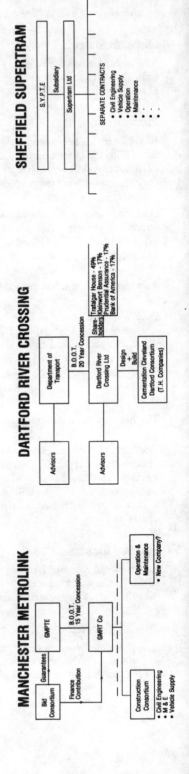

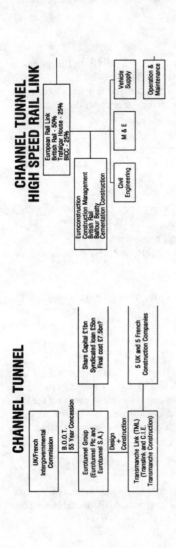

mately 60% is street running with the remainder on segregated track. The capital cost is estimated at £85m. A second line from the city centre to Meadowhall is planned which is awaiting Royal Assent. We understand that the project will be run by Supertram Ltd which will place a number of separate contracts – apparently keeping the main interface and revenue risks themselves.

4. **London Underground – Jubilee Line**

It is clear that major extensions to the system and capacity of LUL are required particularly to connect to the Docklands Light Railway has performed a sterling service but much greater capacity will be required when some of the new office buildings are completed. One concept considered was for private groups to construct, own and operate a heavy underground system from Waterloo to Greenwich and Canary Wharf but it was decided that the interface with the rest of the London Underground system methods of operation, safety and revenue sharing means that such an extension will have to be managed by London Underground, hence the announced extension of the Jubilee Line through Canary Wharf area to Stratford. It seems likely that there will be some contribution to the capital investment from those most likely to benefit from this new line. Other new lines are under construction and there may be opportunities for private companies to invest.

5. **London Underground – Central Line**

In addition to the planned extension to the Jubilee Line and others, work is currently underway to improve the Central Line, both refurbishing the line itself and control equipment and supplying new rolling stock. This is in effect a variation of the project management contract in which John Brown, a Trafalgar House subsidiary, has a project services contract.

Under this contract, John Brown will be responsible for a wide range of services. Working closely with London Underground, John Brown will provide project controls, such as programming, cost controls and financial reporting using the latest computerised systems. The contract also covers technical coordination and interface management, procurement and commercial services, construction supervision,

safety and quality assurance. Work has already started in the offices of London Underground and in John Brown's London office. The project is due for completion in 1996.

The Central Line presently carries half a million passengers a day and sections of the line are among the busiest in the underground system. Demand is forecast to grow by a further 20% over the next ten years.

The project includes the provision of 680 railcars of modern design with lightweight bodies, bright interiors and improved passenger information systems. Prototypes of these trains have been in passenger service on the Jubilee Line for almost a year.

A new signalling system incorporating automatic train control will be installed, having already been evaluated by London Underground. Improvements will include savings in electrical energy, continuous monitoring of trains to facilitate mainte-nance, and provision of closed circuit TV (CCTV) on all platforms and trains. The opportunity will also be taken to enhance power supplies, upgrade depots, provide additional sidings and make improvements to tracks and tunnels.

The contract for the 680 vehicles has been awarded to BREL Ltd.

6. **High Speed Rail Link, Channel Tunnel**

The following slide (diagram) illustrates a possible contractual structure for the high speed rail link. It was announced in October 1989 that a joint venture of BR, BICC and Trafalgar House would develop this high speed link as a privately funded operation. This project is still at the early stages of design and seeking of consents. However, the point to note is that the same partners are in the overall owning company as in the construction consortium. This is in marked contrast to the structure for the construction of the Channel Tunnel, illustrated on the next slide.

For the high speed link Euro Construction will be the project manager responsible for design, construction and procurement on behalf of the client. Each contract will be let out to tender by Trafalgar House and BICC and their respective subsidiaries will be able to tender, there being a BR right of veto. A separate company is being established to operate and maintain the rail link.

In the case of the Channel Tunnel the client, Eurotunnel represents the investors. The contractor, Trans Manche Link is a consortium of ten British and French contractors. The arguments between the two sides have been well aired in recent weeks as illustrated by Mr Peter Costain's letter to Mr Morton. There appear to be too many tiers of management, poor communications and no agreement or mechanism.

7. **Dartford**

The contractual structure for the Dartford Bridge is shown on the following slide (diagram). DRC is 49% Trafalgar House and the balance a number of banks and institutional investors. The Department of Transport as the controlling party is advised by Mott MacDonald and DRC by Halcrow. DRC has placed a contract with a joint venture of Cementation Construction and Cleveland Bridge Engineering. Other Trafalgar House companies are subcontractors. There is one organisation effectively responsible for the design and construction of the project. This bridge is well into construction helped by a long fine summer and a relatively mild winter.

8. **Tyne & Wear Metro**

The Tyne & Wear Metro was executed in pre-Thatcherite times but is interesting to have a quick look at. This was in effect controlled and managed in the public sector. The Tyne & Wear PTE acted as project manager with Mott Hay & Anderson project co-ordinator.

The project organisation was described in Prov. Inst. Civ. Engineers Part I 1981 Nov. 669-693.

The original capital cost estimate was £65.5m at January 1972 prices excluding design fees, site supervision and contingencies for non-civil engineering works.

The revised cost was £170.1m by November 1975.

5. CONCLUSIONS

I have in this paper sketched some of the contractural forms being used and where there may be an imbalance between risk and profit.

– Private company participation implies that a profit is to be made.

– Government support is essential in order to see that the time required for planning and legislative approval is minimised.

– In many cases there must be a subsidy to ensure viability.

ACKNOWLEDGEMENTS

CENTRO
16 Summer Lane
Birmingham B19 3SD

Discussion on papers 10 – 15

J. WILLIS, London Regional Transport
I would like to make a few points about the Parliamentary process with which I have been closely involved over the past 5 years.
As Mr Claydon has pointed out in Paper 13, the process is getting more difficult. There are three reasons for this: (i) the sheer number of Bills; (ii) interest in the private Bill process from MPs and (iii) public interest in our proposals, particularly the environmental issues. The system needs to change, but for the time being we have to live with it.
I offer some advice to those embarking on the process. In the past the deposit of the Bill has been the start of the process. I believe this is no longer possible and at least 18 months are required for preparation, consultation and negotiation.

(1) Preparation. The Bill and Parliamentary plans tell people little about the proposal - so it is essential to produce a number of documents before depositing the Bill which explains the proposal, including route plans, station layouts, artists impressions and the environmental impact statement.

(2) Anticipate public concern. Flush these out by public consultation, leaflets and meetings. Consultation must be done, be seen to be done and it should be consultation not just information.

(3) With respect to any lawyers, keep them out until the last possible moment. Informal unprejudiced discussions can achieve a lot more than formal confrontation.

(4) If petitions are presented, get behind the legal jargon, find out the specific concerns and seek solutions. Broad `environmental concerns' expressed in a petition may be

solved by a simple noise barrier and planting a few
Leylandii.

(5) Agree technical issues before the committee sits. The
last thing a committee wants is to have two consultant
engineers arguing over the price of concrete.

(6) Remember the committee is made up of politicians. MPs
are swayed by emotion which most pressure groups use to
great effect.

(7) Talk to everybody. Many people feel we use the
Parliamentary process to avoid public inquiries. If
people have been properly consulted and a mechanism for
continuing discussion is in place _before_ deposit of the
Bill there will be less complaint about the process.
Most importantly work with the local authority and not
against them.

I see the next few years as far as Parliamentary Bills are
concerned being particularly difficult. On the DLR Beckton
extension we had 10 petitions and it took 33 months to get the
Bill through Parliament. We have received 95 petitions
against the Jubilee Line Bill deposited last November and at
the same rate it will take us 25 years to get the Jubilee Line
Bill through! The large number of petitions may have
something to do with the limited preparation time (less than 6
months) before the Bill was deposited.

My message is therefore simple. Time spent before a Bill
is deposited is time saved after.

R. F. DIXON, _Paper 10_

I would like to endorse Mr Willis's advice to start
preparation for a Bill well before deposit but would take
issue with him about keeping lawyers out of the preparations
until the last possible moment. While sharing his healthy
reluctance to use the legal profession, there are times when
their presence can concentrate the mind of a possible objector
and shorten what could have been a protracted discussion.

C. B. CLAYDON, _Paper 13_

While I would agree with Mr Willis that lawyers are best
kept away from discussions with the outside world for as long
as possible, it is vitally important for a promoter to have
consulted them beforehand and so be well-versed in the
strengths and weaknesses of his legal position before engaging
in discussions with third parties. In this way he may avoid

240

giving way unnecessarily on important issues.

A. ROWE, AEA Technology

Increasingly, major operators (e.g. BR, LUL) are applying formal safety assessment techniques to help them in quantifying the safety risk of their operations. Stages in a safety risk assessment are

(a) hazard identification. (What can go wrong?)
(b) Frequency assessment. (How often will it go wrong?)
(c) Consequence assessment. (What will happen?)
(d) Risk evaluation. (What does it all mean? What can we do about it?)

In essence, we need to quantify the safety risk in order to address the areas which will reduce the frequency or mitigate the consequences to the greatest degree for the amount of money available.

It is a truism that the sooner you pay attention to safety, the cheaper it is over the long term. Formal methods, including safety risk assessment and attention to good safety management systems help to achieve this goal.

C.B. HOLDEN, Paper 14

I accept entirely what Mr Rowe says about formal safety assessment techniques. The point is that each of his stages can be and should be used as appropriate not only before building an LRT system - i.e. at the design stage - but also after it has opened. Safety assessment is a task which must be regarded as a continuous process.

I. HARRIS, Greater Manchester PTE

On the issue of safety standards, there is a danger that the adoption of unduly high standards for rail systems will price off such systems and force people to use much less safe alternative modes. Is there not a need for some agreed safety standards for each mode, even though they may not be identical for all modes?

In response to Mr Ashburner's comments on Manchester Metrolink, it is important to note that the design-build-maintain approach was not recommended by Greater Manchester PTE or its merchant banking advisors. We would have preferred a separate design and build contract and an operating contract. Alternatively we proposed that the infrastructure be owned by the PTE and the private sector would run and operate the vehicles, on a similar basis to bus operations.

These were rejected by Government simply because they did not transfer enough risk to the private sector.

C.B. Holden, Paper 14

The safety standards which have to be observed are those which are demanded by the general public. Those who operate transport systems in the public sector have to accept that these standards will be inequitable. More is demanded of those systems which are already perceived to be safe; less of those where the user has more direct and personal involvement in the safety of the system. However deplorable this attitude of double standards may be, the Railway Inspectorate has to respond to what the public demand, or, where something new is proposed, to what their experience dictates will be the demand. That does not stop the Inspectorate from trying to educate the public into making sensible and reasonable demands for safety in public transport systems.

E. Lawrence, Eurocap –Transportech

I wish to add a few points to those of Major Holden.

(1) As well as the 'jerk rate' associated with braking, there is another force which comes as a result of rapid acceleration, and this may need control on some types of traction systems.

(2) Automatic doors not fitted with pressure sensors are referred to as 'Dragons Jaws' in some continental cities. The closing force can cause distress to the elderly and disabled.

(3) Passengers standing on the moving floor section of articulated vehicles during rush hours can experience disturbing forces. On a 25 m diameter curve the amount of movement at the circumference of the moving place can be considerable.

(4) On some trams there is no external signal given when the driver of the vehicle has cancelled the door opening mechanism prior to departure. I have seen intending passengers running alongside a moving vehicle trying to get the doors open.

(5) Some trams are fitted with floor buttons which operate the alarm bell inside the passenger compartments. This can lead to accidental operation of the alarm bell causing annoyance and unnecessary attention to pedestrians and other vehicle drivers in the proximity of

the tram. Exuberant children do, on occasions, take
advantage of this facility. Clearly the button should be
made inoperative under normal conditions.

The above, while referring to comfort rather than safety,
are only some of the examples gathered by a veteran rider of
many LRT vehicles on the continent.

C.B. Holden, Paper 14

Mr Lawrence has put forward an interesting list of pitfalls
for a vehicle designer to avoid. The forces imposed on a
passenger, whether from acceleration, braking or turning, has
to be imposed in such a way that the passenger can respond
appropriately or by limiting them so that a passenger is not
caught unawares. Door closing arrangements are notoriously
difficult to get right and Mr Lawrence has mentioned two out
of many aspects. The first on the closing force is well-known
but the second on the need for an external as well as an
internal warning that 'doors enabled' has been cancelled is
less widely recognized.

B. H. NORTH, Travers Morgan

Hong Kong Mass Transit Corporation were very PR conscious
and the Chairman employed professional PR consultants to
'sell' the Metro to a public which had never seen or used an
underground railway before. After due study, the consultants
presented an advertising logo (a symbolic tree) and an
accompanying slogan 'Growing for you'. While disliked by the
Engineering and Operational Committee, the Chairman decided to
adopt the proposals. The tree and the slogan appeared on
posters, on all site hoardings, on TV and in the newspapers.
It was a huge success. The moral is - use people who are
professionally experienced PR consultants, if you want to be
sure to get your message across.

C. F. BONNETT, formerly Docklands Light Railway, now London Transport International

I would like to express various comments in the light of the
experience of the initial railway at Docklands. We found it
essential to consult with the public at all stages and to keep
plugging away at educating the local people. This can be done
in many ways but we found a regular newspaper including news
of progress of the railway and articles from members of the
project team to be most effective. Distribution was very
effective and was done on special family days when we invited
all the staff and their families to take part, paying a
nominal sum to even the youngest.

Mr Ringer's comments on noise are most important. On the initial DLR we found noise was greater than expected and as a result there was much debate with local pressure groups and in Committee. The Bill of the Beckton extension was only passed into law when LRT gave a formal undertaking to Parliament to keep noise to a certain level, to monitor it and also to adopt a noise code which included ongoing measures such as rail grinding and wheel turning when and if levels exceeded those laid down.

In conclusion, with reference to Major Holden's paper, The Railway Inspectorate can be most helpful, but it is essential that they are involved at the earliest stage with regular progress meetings as the project evolves.

R. F. DIXON, Paper 10

I endorse Mr Bonnett's plea that the Railway Inspectorate should be involved at the very earliest stage and then regularly updated. I consider that this approach has been of great assistance to the Midland Metro planning phases.

C. REES, De Leuw, Cather International Ltd

Based on De Leuw, Cather's involvement in the planning, design and construction of most of the LRTs developed recently in the United States, the following guidelines are offered when planning and promoting the development of light transit systems.

Have an orderly assessment process. We are lucky in the US. The Federal Government has set out guidelines for assessing the feasibility of rail transit projects. This includes assessment in stages, with a minimum set of patronage and economic benefit threshold values for eligibility at an early stage together with a mandatory requirement that the system under study should be part of an approved regional transportation plan; prior agreement on demand forecasting, costing, and environmental assessment procedures; and consideration of no-build and traffic systems management options as part of the transit alternatives assessment process. Adherence to these rules by Government agency sponsors and consultants has at least assured projects of equal treatment at the Federal level at which most transit projects are funded.

Know your markets. The largest market for light transit will remain bus and rail users, who will constitute 50% or more of future patronage. They use transit for economic and social reasons. They are your local residents along proposed routes. They must not become NIMBYs so their concerns must be listened to through a structured community involvement process. The

second most important market is car drivers. They respond to
time and cost savings, so speed and door to door travel time
and convenience are important. Transit vehicles caught in
congestion will not appeal to them. The third most important
market is the development community who must support future
growth plans and who may be required to fund elements of the
project. They respond to better accessibility, enhanced
markets and increased rents. The fourth market is Government
agencies who fund and administer parts of the urban
infrastructure. Cost and economic efficiency and control are
their main concerns. They will not use the transit system,
but they are a key to successfully passing through the
approval process. Keeping the interests of all constituencies
in mind is important when selling a project.
Keep it simple. Our many systems and technology appraisals
have taught us one main thing. Exotic and complex systems are
expensive to build and maintain and you have to pay more for
tailor-made systems. A prime example are the Channel Tunnel
tourist shuttle trains which are running at £40 million each.

So many LRTs have been implemented in the US because
conventional lower cost approaches were used to solve
problems. Based upon my direct experience in four major light
transit projects in the Washington DC area, I would recommend
that serious consideration be given to

(a)   converting existing rail and utility lines to transit
(b)   single tracking major route segments where headways
      exceed 10 minutes one way
(c)   conventional overhead power supply and signal controls
(d)   at-grade crossings wherever practicable
(e)   simple self-service fare collection without complex
      equipment and gates
(f)   off-the-shelf vehicles on at least a standardized design
      for UK applications.

With these guidelines in mind I am sure that many of the
projects in the planning stage will advance more quickly to
implementation than might otherwise have been the case.

T. D. HAMILTON, Durham County Council
The papers by Messrs Dixon and Claydon highlight the
problems facing promoters of light rail schemes in the United
Kingdom: that they have no examples and face opposition from a
number of quarters. The problems are not new and organized
opposition has been one of the features of major highway
schemes since the early 1970s. The Department of Transport
has developed procedures to attempt to explain the
justification for the choice of a particular route but relies
on the provisions of the highways legislation to achieve an

end result. They do not need to obtain fresh acts of
Parliament to build a motorway.

The challengers to the 19th century procedures which have
faced light rail promoters show the benefits of more recent
legislation. However, I consider that light rail should have
more supporters than opponents and the task is one of
galvanizing support. The successful introduction of light
rail in the French provincial cities of Lille, Lyon, Grenoble,
Marseille and Nantes was not accomplished without effort, <u>but</u>
they are now textbook examples and much visited by local
authority officers and members from the United Kingdom. I see
Grenoble or Nantes trams used in several of the booklets
produced in the United Kingdom to illustrate and promote light
rail schemes.

The programme of public consultations needs to have as wide
a catchment as possible and should be well beyond the route
and the opposition from people who may lose property or could
suffer blight.
Grenoble established a Committee to obtain the views of the
mobility handicapped and took them through the development
stages from vehicle design to access at stations. This not
only ensured that the end product was user friendly but
established a `league of friends'.

Perhaps in these days of charter flights it would be
acceptable for sponsors of LRT schemes in Britain to take
groups to France or Germany or Switzerland to see for
themselves. The groups can include the disabled as well as
the people who would be directly affected. The process must
be one of education - if I were to choose I would suggest
Grenoble.

Progress has been more rapid in France with a Government
committed to freeing the cities of traffic congestion and
reducing atmospheric pollution. The existence of the local
employers tax, the Versment Transport, which makes a
contribution to LRT construction and operation, is one of the
very factors in harnessing local involvement and support.

16. Operating a light railway in Britain

J. R. GATES, MIEE, Operations Director, Docklands Light Railway

INTRODUCTION

1. Most of the effort that goes into the advanced planning of a new LRT system concentrates on the provision of infrastructure. The key planning issues are the alternative alignments, whether the system will be roadrunning, fully segregated or hybrid, steel wheel on steel rail or rubber tyred guideway, and the extent to which existing road or rail alignment can be used.

2. The operator generally arrives on the scene after these fundamental decisions have been made and then has the job of transforming a kit of parts into a living entity. The ingredients that the operator adds include:

   Service   -   the method by which the infrastructure is used to satisfy passenger needs,

   People   -   selection and training of the team to operate the service,

   Culture   -   the particular style in which the operating company performs its' role.

3. The only existing examples of LRT systems in the UK are Docklands Light Railway and Tyne and Wear Metro (if we exclude People Movers and Blackpool Trams). Both Docklands and Tyne and Wear bear little resemblance to other currently planned schemes. They both operate on segregated tracks, use conventional steel wheels and rails, and could be better described as Light Rapid Transit rather than Light Rail.

They are also very different from each other, with Tyne and Wear utilising automatic train protection (ATP) and central supervision but with manual control, whilst DLR is a fully automated ALRT system railway but with one person on board each train to close doors, check tickets, and drive if necessary in an emergency.

4. Opening a new LRT System provides its operator with a unique opportunity to change people's perceptions of public transport. With new brightly painted vehicles, a newly recruited and highly motivated workforce, and the media interest surrounding the opening, a high profile is generated. The ability to create a new 'culture' depends largely on how the operating organisation is set up. It was decided to create a separate subsidiary company of London Regional Transport to operate DLR, completely independent of London Underground. This allowed a completely new approach to staffing policy for DLR which has been one of its main successes.

5. In the case of Tyne and Wear although a new organisation was formed within the PTE, it is not a limited company. Whilst it appeared to start with a clean sheet of paper it did nevertheless inherit many of its practices through staff who were displaced from jobs in British Rail and the local bus company. This restricted Metro's ability to introduce a new forward looking personnel policy.

6. Although a new Light Railway might be very small it must still comply with all the statutory requirements of a large railway. Principal amongst these is safeguarding the safety of passengers and staff. There is now a greater emphasis on audit of safety management following the recent serious accidents in public transport, and this imposes additional demands on the organisation.

    If the operating organisation is established as a separate company it is also necessary to provide all the other normal business functions to support the core business.

ORGANISATION AND STAFFING

7. The present organisation of Docklands Light Railway Limited is shown below. The shape and size of the organisation is changing to reflect the growth of the railway. For some time to come a substantial part of the Company's activities will be associated with extending the railway, and managing the interface between the operating railway and construction works absorbs a large proportion of available effort.

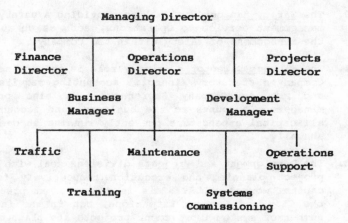

Organisation of Docklands Light Railway Limited   October 1989

8.   The <u>Operations</u> division runs the core business.   This includes:

-    <u>Traffic</u>, which operate the train services, protect revenue and provide information to passengers.

-    <u>Maintenance</u>, which maintains all infrastructure, vehicles, systems and equipment.

-    <u>Operations Support</u>, which produces and maintains operating procedures, performs service planning, monitors service performance and co-ordinates engineering work taking place on the railway.

-    There are also separate <u>operational training</u>, and <u>systems commissioning</u> functions during the period of expansion.

9.   The <u>Business</u> division provides support to the core business including:

-    Business planning

-    Marketing and PR

-    Personnel management

-    Supplies management

-    Safety management

10. The <u>Safety Manager</u>, as well as providing a safety management service to Operations, acts as an audit on the management of safety within the Company.

11. The <u>Finance Director's</u> primary role is to service the Company's statutory financial accounting requirements, and act as Company Secretary. He also provides management accounts to the business, and accounts for all capital expenditure presently running at over £80m annually.

12. The <u>Development</u> and <u>Projects</u> divisions deal with project planning and execution respectively for all capital works on DLR. This is dominated at present by the City and Beckton Extensions, but in the future a number of system improvement projects are planned.

Staffing Policy

13. As a new company, DLR has been able to set new standards and policies in the way people are employed. All staff are paid 4 weekly salaries and work a 35 hour week. Pay and conditions are negotiated by elected Company Councillors at an annual Managing Director's Meeting. Other industrial relations matters and grievances are dealt with at regular Company Council meetings. Since 1988 the Company Councillors have been advised by a Trades Union, and a full time official of EESA (a division of the EETPU) attends the Managing Director's Meeting.

14. It is also the policy of the Company to use Quality Circles and Team Briefing to promote participation for staff in decision making, and to maintain satisfactory two way communications between staff and management. These concepts can be difficult to organise in a public transport operation due to extensive shiftwork and the mobility of staff, but DLR regard staff involvement as a high priority, and it is particularly important during a period of expansion.

Staffing of Operations

Traffic

15. DLR recruits its traffic staff locally in East London. When the railway was first opened recruitment took place at all grades, but increasingly the Supervisory and Management posts are filled through promotion from junior grades. As it is DLR policy to recruit the best people available at each level most vacancies are advertised internally and externally concurrently. Selection of staff is supported by aptitude and personality tests followed by interviews by the line manager.

16. An unusual mix of qualities is required by Train Captains who provide DLR's customer interface and therefore need the personality and attitude necessary for dealing effectively with all types of people. They also need the mental and physical ability to cope with an emergency. Although they can be in immediate contact with the Control Room they nevertheless have to display authority in a crisis. So far DLR has managed to find sufficient people to meet these requirements, but of course they all have strengths and weaknesses and the aim is to have a balanced team overall with all staff meeting basic standards in all aspects of the job.

17. Recruitment of traffic staff is almost continuous due to the expansion of the service and the success of junior staff in being identified for more senior positions. Of the original 42 Train Captains 13 have risen to supervisory or junior management posts.

18. As the railway grows in size and intensity of operation, the jobs will change. The role of Traffic Supervisor, who controls the service centrally, will change significantly and future requirements are now influencing recruitment.

Maintenance

19. DLR staff perform varying degrees of railway maintenance depending on the discipline.

Discipline	Failure Repairs	Routine Maintenance	Component Overhaul
Rolling Stock	DLR	DLR	External
Signal & Telecom	DLR	DLR	External
Central Control System	DLR	External	External
AFC	DLR	DLR	External
Traction Power	External	External	External
Lifts & Escalators	External	External	External
Permanent Way	DLR	DLR/External	External
Buildings & Structures	External	External	External
Building Services	DLR/External	DLR/External	External

20. With the building of Beckton maintenance depot DLR will increase its own capacity and capability. An underfloor wheel lathe will be provided and a rail grinding machine. It is probable that electronic component repair and testing for vehicles and signalling will become economic. The present position with varying stages of warranty covering the vehicles and signalling systems has delayed decisions on this.

21. DLR's policy on maintenance is to examine each new demand to see whether it can be accommodated within the existing available resources or whether it is necessary and more economic to contract out the work.

22. Because of the particular requirements of DLR, it has been necessary to provide additional training to supplement the varied experience of technical recruits. Also the learning curve of technicians has continued throughout the first two years of operation and it has been possible to increase the range and depth of tasks undertaken during the period.

23   As the operating organisation grows and matures it is
      necessary to re-consider the original staffing
      concepts. The concept of a multi-disciplinary
      workforce must be reviewed as the size of the railway
      and the technical complexity of the maintenance tasks
      increase. It is necessary to strike a balance at each
      stage of development to achieve reliable service at
      economic cost.

      DLR is currently addressing the degree of
      specialisation of its maintenance staff which can be
      illustrated by this simple diagram.

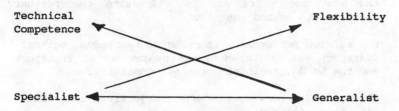

24.   The cost of maintaining an automatic railway designed
      for low initial cost can be high. Whilst the
      performance specification can set reliability and
      maintenance cost targets, the reality is that it is
      only by including operations and maintenance in the
      scope of supply that the contractor can be really tied
      down. We all will watch closely how the
      Design-Build-Operate scheme works in Manchester,
      although of course, it has to be a very long trial.

      DLR is going in the opposite direction with the
      construction of the Beckton Extension and using the
      conventional Client Engineer's Design method of
      contract. DLR will exercise tight control over design
      and build standards to achieve satisfactory operability
      and maintainability of the final railway. This approach
      has been recently shown elsewhere to create a far
      greater degree of confidence on the part of the
      operator, that he can control the end result,
      particularly where the work being undertaken impacts on
      an existing operating railway.

PROVIDING THE SERVICE

25.   All new LRT operators will have to meet performance
      objectives irrespective of the type of system and the
      modus operandi of the operating organisation. In the
      Design-Build-Operate system these objectives will form
      part of the contract specification. In the case of
      owner operation the relationship between service
      performance objectives and system capability may be
      more tenuous.

26. The DLR Initial Railway was designed for a maximum
capacity of 1750 passengers per hour in either
direction on its two main branches, provided through a
7.5 minute service with 9 single articulated LRVs. It
is now being upgraded to a capacity of 13,000 per hour
in one direction with potential for a further expansion
to 20,000.

This increase will be achieved equally through
lengthening the trains and through higher frequencies.
According to latest passenger forecasts, DLR will
be only just keeping pace with increases in demand in
the next two years and is addressing the further
increases in demand post 1992.

27. DLR service performance is measured by London Regional
Transport and monitored by the Department of Transport
and the London Regional Passenger Committee.

The key indicators against which objectives have been
set are as follows:

1. Mileage   -   percentage of schedule achieved.

2. Reliability   -   achievement of service frequency

3. Ticket Machines   -   availability

4. Lifts & Escalators   -   availability

5. Cleaning of Trains   -   frequency of internal and
external cleaning.

28. The fact that DLR is presently required to perform at
the peak of its capacity and performance at a time when
Upgrading work introduces new 'teething problems' with
new or modified equipment, places a strain on meeting
performance objectives.

29. Fitting train operation schedules to meet customer
needs is an important consideration. Clearly every
system has operating constraints by way of maximum
length of trains and minimum headways.

Within these constraints the operator must aim to match
the service to meet passenger needs. DLR has
experience of this in operating special services for
the London Arena entertainment venue, and in running
special services from Stratford into the City during
the BR and LUL strikes in 1989. Both of these events
involved the operation of abnormal schedules and
routes.

UPGRADEABILITY

30. One of the commonly accepted characteristics of LRT is
     the ability to build a small minimum viable system and
     expand later to meet demand. This theory is not so well
     proved with ALRTs. The theory holds well for street
     running systems as the marginal cost of adding route
     miles can be quite low.

31. In the case of DLR there are a number of features of
     its expansion that are unique. The first of these is
     that the upgrade and extensions to the Bank and Beckton
     include a fundamental remodelling of its delta junction
     at the centre of the system. This, combined with the
     upgrade of the ATS system mean that in human terms it
     is like performing a combined operation for heart
     transplant and brain surgery, whilst simultaneously
     fitting an artificial limb. In some ways the situation
     is more severe than a medical operation in that not
     only is the survival of the patient being maintained
     but he is also being required to perform an
     increasingly heavy days work between stages of the
     operation.

32. The second feature that tests the theory of
     Upgradeability is tunnelling to Bank which is as
     complex as any performed for the construction of a
     rapid transit system. The DLR platforms will be the
     deepest in London and the tunnellers have had to
     penetrate ground densely populated with all conceivable
     statutory services, other underground railway tunnels
     and the foundations of some of London's most historic
     buildings. In addition, halfway through the job it has
     been necessary to make changes to meet new requirements
     following the Fennell enquiry into the Kings Cross
     Fire.

33. Many other aspects of the Initial System have to be
     improved or modified to meet the ten-fold increase in
     demand now being planned for. These include:

     -    vehicle doors which on the Initial System were of
          a type not designed for repetitive crush loads.
          All new vehicles purchased will have sliding
          rather than pivoted doors.

     -    the need to use unsignalled `Emergency Shunt' to
          move a vehicle to the docking point at a station,
          in the event that it fails in ATO mode. New
          deliveries of rolling stock will have the facility
          to reset into ATP mode to allow full line speed to
          be used to the next station.

- end doors will be provided on vehicles for multiple-unit running. This will enable the Train Captain to reach the emergency driving position without having to leave the train when transferring from rear to front vehicle.

34. Many other features are being improved including improving the robustness of the central ATS system and provision of more recovery capacity in the timetabling.

INTEGRATION WITH OTHER PUBLIC TRANSPORT

35. There were some compromises built into DLR when it was constructed. Unlike Tyne and Wear Metro which was largely built around bus/rail interchanges and intermodal ticketing, DLR interchanges are less convenient.

    This arises mainly from a difference of purpose for which the systems were built. Whereas Tyne and Wear Metro was constructed to relieve road congestion into the centre of Newcastle and to encourage people onto public transport, DLR was conceived for quite a different and specific purpose, to provide in effect a local light rail system to service and support the redevelopment of Docklands. In this role it has been singularly successful as the ever increasing passenger demand shows.

36. The DLR ticketing system is designed to suit the present situation whereby 75% of passengers already have valid LT Travelcards or through tickets from LUL or BR when arriving on the system. The pair of ticket machines provided at each of the 15 unstaffed stations are therefore capable of issuing only single journey tickets.

37. Both Tyne and Wear and DLR operate a penalty fare system with no ticket checks at stations.
    Tyne and Wear have abandoned their original automatic ticket barriers which were found not to be cost effective at unstaffed stations.

    Success with penalty fares depends on the ability to handle the administration and follow up of defaulters. Tyne and Wear are better placed to do this in that they have a less volatile and more localised patronage than does DLR.

CONCLUSIONS

38. The experience of operating DLR and Tyne and Wear Metro can be sharply contrasted. However, both have exceeded the expectations of their sponsors in terms of passenger demand and revenue generation. Both have brought new passengers to public transport and are generally popular with their users.

39. Tyne and Wear went for a conventional solution and the Metro is physically almost indistinguishable from a small suburban railway.
DLR on the other hand was a bold attempt to do something new. Whilst all the components of its automatic system had been used successfully elsewhere, the particular mix and the degree of complexity is unique.

   DLR started out with a number of new concepts and the extent to which these concepts have been successful is as follows:

40. **Automatic trains and Train Captain on board to check tickets.**

   Full automatic operation is far easier to apply to downtown people movers and simple straight line rapid transits. The delta junction and single running sections of DLR make efficient train regulation complex, but automatic operation has facilitated the Train Captain concept which has been the biggest success of DLR. It has proved that it is possible to employ and train staff who interface well with passengers, whilst at the same time dealing with the safety and operational aspects of the job, and get to work at 04.30 hours to put the first train into service.

41. **Open stations, ticket vending machines, ticket inspection on trains, penalty fares**

   Despite the large proportion of DLR passengers who do not need to purchase tickets when joining the system, ticket vending at stations has proved to be a critical feature of the passenger service at stations. The DLR system has worked generally well but ticket machines will be enhanced in future by the addition of a notechanging facility. Also separate validation of tickets has given way to integral validation by the ticket machine on issue.

42. Open stations, Safety and Security

The open station concept has worked well on DLR.
Unlike Tyne and Wear, vandalism and crime at stations
has been minimal. This is thought to result from the
open 'see through' aspect of most DLR stations coupled
with relatively high lighting levels and remote
surveillance. Regular and dedicated police presence
also plays an important part.

43. Disabled provision

The provision of station lifts, level boarding and
wheelchair bays in vehicles has proved popular with the
aged and mobility impaired (and by mothers with
pushchairs!). The lifts have not proved to be
sufficiently robust for unstaffed stations, and
equipment status monitoring is to be improved in
future.

44. Steel wheels, steel rails, tight curves

Wheel and rail wear has been less than expected. Some
selected rail grinding has taken place on two
occasions in two years, and wheel turning is performed
at intervals of 18 months at the present service level.

17. Running light railways; experience in Europe

M. BONZ, Regierungbaumeister, Technisches
Vorstandsmitglied, Stuttgarter Strassenbahnen AG

SYNOPSIS. In European countries the methods of operation of
existing light rail transit systems have their origin in the
former tramway systems or follow the example of the chiefly
multi-mode public transport executives. Operations under direct
local authority and limited companies with a majority of public
partners predominate. Based on positive and negative experiences with these existing systems, some requirements relevant
to new operations are outlined. The paper ends with a more detailed presentation of the operational conditions of a German
light rail transit system.

DIFFERENT STARTING-CONDITIONS

1. Before comparing the methods of operation of light rail
transit systems in Europe, the following question has to be
asked: Are the conditions under which light rail transit
systems were introduced comparable? The answer to this question
reveals an essential difference that has to be discussed first.

2. There are light rail transit systems which had originally opened decades ago as conventional electric tramways. They
represent an uninterrupted development of a traditional system.
The reasons for changing to light rail transport technology are
obvious:

(a) A modern light rail system can ease congestion in the
cities.
(b) Improving public transport service through addition of a
modern light rail transit system, makes it more attractive to passengers. Increased patronage, in turn, leads
to better econimic results.
(c) Planned extensions of the network require investments
anyway.
(d) Or simply, the rolling stock needs renewing.

3. The introduction of a light rail system could be an entirely fresh start for public transport services by rail if
there has never been such a system or if, as seen more often,
a former tramway system was abandoned years ago. In the latter
case, the time gap makes a completely new introduction of the
system necessary. The main reasons for interest in a new light
rail system are:

(a) Replacing existing bus services by a more capable and more cost-effective system.
(b) Expected effects on intermodal interchange as an important measure to reduce congestion.
(c) Favouring land development projects.

4.   These different starting-conditions affect the methods of operation of a light rail transit system. If there has been a continuous development from a traditional tramway system to a modern light rail transit system a change in the way of running the system is not very likely. If, for example, the former tramway system operated under local authority or was run by a limited company, the existing method of operation is likely to remain unchanged. A look at the situation on the European continent supports this statement. In European cities most light rail transit systems are based on existing tramway systems. They kept their method of operation from the former system. Even systems without a traditional link, e. g. Grenoble (France), Lausanne (Switzerland), became a department of the existing passsenger transport executive. An exceptional case is the situation in the French city of Lille, where operation of the metro has been delegated to a private company taking a light rail vehicle manufacturer into the partnership.
5.   As for the situation in the UK, apart from Blackpool there were no existing tramway systems. Therefore the light rail transit systems in operation or under development were free to choose their methods of operation without prejudice. This may make it easier to decide on the most suitable way to run a new system. In addition, the present UK government is not at all receptive to any idea that would require an increase in public expenditure. At first sight, these less traditional links and the political aim of minimizing the public sector's involvement in the light rail transit projects are affecting new UK operations.
6.   But does it mean the conditions in the UK differ from those on the European continent in such a significant way that an interchange of experience in methods of operation does not make sense?
7.   That is not the case. The fact is that authorities responsible for management and operation of light rail transit systems in Europe today are mainly transport executives which are run as a department of local government agencies, or are limited companies with a majority holding municipal partner. From the experience with these dominant methods of operation insights can be gained that may assist the decision making process in the UK. So this paper will not be a summary of competing methods of operation, rather it will try to point out some requirements, which ought to be satisfied in order to guarantee effective operation. Towards this end the positive and negative aspects of certain methods will be shown.

FIRST REQUIREMENT

8. The institution responsible for the operation of a light rail transit system should be in a position to affect inter-acting components of urban traffic.

9. Most existing light rail transit systems in Europe have guideways, that are not completely separated from road traffic. Giving up generally segregated operation has the economic bene-fit of lowering capital costs for public transport ways. In addition, it is an important condition for more flexible im-plementation of the system in cities. But it requires demand responding signal control for the light rail transit systems including priority at level crossings and at sites where light rail vehicles share lanes with road traffic. Based on experi-ence this often causes a conflict of interests. The light rail transport executives must be in a position to carry out their measures to reduce trip time and avoid intermediate stops in addition to the regular ones.

10. The most promising method of operation to ensure this is a municipal government operated light rail transit system, be-cause the reconciliation of divergent interests has to be done within the municipal authorities. Usually these are the same municipal institutions which had to authorize the investment for the light rail transit system. So these authorities are easier to convince that the effectiveness of the system depends on their further decisions.

11. A similar assessment of the advantages of government operated systems follows from the more general problem, of how to withstand competition from private transport. A passenger transport executive must be able to prevent apparent distor-tions of competing conditions, such as increasing the capacity of roads parallel to light rail transit lines. In West-Germany the decisive factor is, that the operating institution becomes a so called "holder of public interest", i. e., it has the right to take part in the final authorisation process for pro-posed (road) projects. A totally private company could never reach such an important position. Its influence on surrounding conditions would be considerably restrained.

SECOND REQUIREMENT

12. In its service area the institution that operates a light rail transit system must be able to have influence on perform-ance and service quality of the supplementary transport systems as well as on fare policy.

13. Many components of public transport itself are affecting the efficiency of a light rail transit system. For the part of the network the design of feeder buslines is required, which deliver and pick up passenger interchanging to and from the light rail system. Competition with parallel running buslines decreases efficiency and should be avoided. A harmonized func-tional planning is necessary.

14. But not only integrated planning has to be considered. Participation in the development of fare structure and in quoting fares is equally important.

15. If planning and fare aspects concerning the whole service area of a light rail transport system can't be covered by the undertaking itself, these functions may be taken over by a transport cooperative. It may create a special organisation to support the more general business for the cooperative's members.

16. In the Netherlands the national government plays the part of such a coordinating organisation. Comparable proceedings are realized in the high density areas of Western Germany, Austria, and Switzerland where integration is served by transport and fare associations as shown below by the example of a German light rail transit system.

17. Delegating non-operational functions to an umbrella organisation which guarantees the interest of the partner seems to be a promising way for allowing private companies to run light rail transit systems.

THIRD REQUIREMENT

18. A light rail transit executive must be prepared to be run as a business enterprise and to appear as such.

19. The outward appearance of light rail transit service mainly depends on its performance and service quality. That includes modern light rail cars, passenger friendly design of stops and stations and the attractiveness of service overall. To succeed in these efforts flexibility in operation is required. Innovations have to be encouraged and out-dated organisational structures must be abandoned. But there is an interrelation between attractive performance and the economic conditions of the enterprise. It must be in a position to rationalize operation, i. e., it must be able to determine its optimized number of personnel and to use the most suitable technical equipment.

20. In this field great advantages are expected from operation methods modeled after the rules for private business enterprises. Nevertheless, the feasibility to introduce equivalent standards at companies owned by the public should not be underrated. Favourable conditions are e. g. repayment of costs caused by activities undertaken for the public good or costs that originated from the construction and maintenance of the public transport way. An actual example is Gothenburg (Sweden), where the existing local authority operations are likely to be commuted to a limited company. The provision and maintenance of the guideway will be left to the city. The light rail transport companies in the West-German Rhine-Ruhr-area look out for similar function sharing. The government of the federal state is willing to assume the cost of infrastructure in order to improve the economic results of the operating companies.

21. Whether a light rail transit system can be run close to the standard of a common business enterprise, also depends on the terms of employment of the staff. In West-Germany in case of authority operations, the complete employment regulations for civil servants have to be considered. That means in spite

of the actual conditions of the labour market, salaries are
fixed including those of the executives. With regard to more
flexibility of the operating institution more incentive regulations are to be preferred, but this generally means to run
the system by a limited company.

FOURTH REQUIREMENT
22. The light rail executive should make use of co-determi-
nation by its employees with the meaning of co-responsibility.
23. Experience from West-Germany reveals that the best way
to achieve this is to have only one trade union as partner.
In Germany this is possible only if all activities in an undertaking can be attached to civil service. It is obvious that
this does hold true in the case of (local) government operation. If the system is run by a limited company it depends on
the kind of partners, who must be public ones by majority. In
Germany a completely private company is not in a position to
manage this. In this respect the method of operation becomes
very important. It is not clear whether the German experience
is transferable to the UK.

STUTTGART - A LIGHT RAIL TRANSIT SYSTEM
REPRESENTATIVE FOR THE SITUATION IN WEST-GERMANY
24. Stuttgart stands for a successful introduction of light
rail service in Germany. Although the starting conditions for
public transport were not very favourable - Stuttgart is the
South-German center of the automobile industry and its topo-
graphy makes transport systems difficult to construct - the
change from tramway to light rail service caused a remarkable
increase in public transport patronage between 15 and 100 %.
Much of this success can be credited to the new light rail twin
car units (DT 8) especially constructed for Stuttgart. Their
comfort and reliability comes close to that of "Mercedes" cars.
At the end of this year the Stuttgart light rail network will
reach 72 line kilometres.
25. This light rail transit system is run by a joint-stock
company, the Stuttgarter Straßenbahnen AG, a traditional transport executive with a tramway department running about 240
articulated tramcar units and a bus department running about
320 busses.
26. To ensure integrated service throughout the greater
Stuttgart area including the suburban railway system (S-Bahn)
run by German Federal Railway, more general functions have been
delegated to a special organisation, the Stuttgart Transport
and Fare Association. This coordinating company is responsible
for

-    transport studies,
-    design of lines and network,
-    scheduling,
-    further development of fare structure,
-    splitting of fare box revenue,
-    transport statistics and
-    public relations.

The functions left to the operating company, which is in partnership with the transport association, are

- all activities necessary to provide safe and orderly
  transport services (system maintenance, duty schedule,
  operating control),
- fare collection,
- technical research and development of the systems.

27. Decisions regarding the transport system (network),
scheduling and fixing transport capacities and fares follow an
agreed sequence: The managing directors of the transport association present their proposals to a supervisory board. It
forms an opinion on the presentation and gives it to the assembly of partners who prepares a resolution.

CONCLUSION
28. Because of the different starting and surrounding conditions for any particular European country a simple recommendation for a certain operation method suitable for UK light
rail systems under development can't be given. The paper shows
that there are several requirements which ought to be considered. On this basis positive and negative aspects of certain
methods can be evaluated. In the end any comparison has to
take the local situation into account.

18. Setting up a new operator

D. S. HELLEWELL, FCIT, FBIM, Director, Greater Manchester Rapid Transit Company

SYNOPSIS

Greater Manchester's Light Rapid Transit system - Metrolink - is the first of the new generation of light rail schemes to include street running. The single contract approach to design, build, operate and maintain Phase I of the system also breaks new ground, not only in the UK, but also overseas. GMM has responsibility for building the system and operating it for fifteen years.

The Paper concentrates on the operational aspects of establishing Metrolink. Reference is made to the consortium that was successful in winning the contract and the establishment of GMM. The structure of the contractual relationships is discussed as are the Company's obligations under the contract.

A feature of the single contract approach is that the design and build and establishment of the operating procedures and organisation go on parallel. The need for close working to ensure that the operator gets the facilities he requires and that, in turn, the technical information is fed back to the operator to ensure that they are reflected in the development of the operating procedures is stressed. The different requirements of the 'railway' and 'street-running' sections are highlighted and discussed.

The organisational structure of the company is considered along with staff recruitment. The commissioning of the technical features must go hand in hand with staff training and testing staff proficiency. The transition from the existing situation to light rail operation is also discussed.

The Paper concludes by looking at the marketing effort for Metrolink and awareness campaigns so that the public may know as much as possible about it. A planned programme to ensure the safety and security of the system for those using it is also outlined.

INTRODUCTION

Greater Manchester's light rail scheme - Metrolink - is the first of the new light rail projects currently being developed in the United Kingdom. As such it is in the vanguard of light rail developments and is pioneering much new ground, technically, financially and institutionally. Other papers have dealt with

the conception and the long gestation of the Manchester scheme
and the detailed contractual and financial elements of it.
Whilst we are pioneering light rail in the UK this mode and its
considerable advantages are well known and understood in Europe
and parts of North America. The assistance and encouragement
received from these organisations and the International Union of
Public Transport (UITP) is gratefully acknowledged.

Government approval, in principle, to Metrolink was given on
18 January 1988 on the basis that the private sector would be
invited to design, build, operator and maintain it. This
approach broke new ground and introduced a number of
opportunities and challenges; all involved have been on a steep
learning curve.

Basically the Client - the PTE - provides a commercial
specification as a point of reference for the Contractor to bid
to. The PTE does sufficient design to be able to estimate the
cost of the project prior to obtaining approval from the PTA and
the DTp. Thereafter the successful Contractor does the detailed
design as a first stage of the job to design, build, operate and
maintain (DBOM) Metrolink. It will be appreciated that it is for
the Contractor to make the trade-offs between lower first cost
and higher ongoing costs of the scheme. With DBOM the Contractor
has to live with the results of the design and build element.
Contractors are used to building to other people's designs and
for the operator to live with the consequences. With DBOM the
"Contractor takes all".

One of the facets of this approach is that the detailed designing
and building must go on hand in hand with the establishment of
operational and maintenance arrangements. It has to be an
iterative process. Likewise the recruitment and training of
staff has to go on simultaneously with design finalisation,
systems development and building, prior to commissioning.

On 27 September 1989 the GMPTA selected the GMA Group. The
members of this consortium are:

   GEC Alsthom Transportation Projects Ltd

   John Mowlem & Company Plc

   Amec Plc

   Greater Manchester Buses Ltd

BACKGROUND

Historically Manchester's railways have terminated at the edge
of the City Centre itself thus requiring passengers to complete
their journeys on foot, by bus or by taxi. Much of Greater
Manchester's rail network is Diesel-operated and in a very run
down condition. It also requires a substantial and increasing
subsidy to keep it going, currently £18M (1989). This does not
increase its capacity or improve its image.

Although the City of Manchester - capital of the North West - is
showing signs of rejuvenation after a difficult period, many
parts of the City and conurbation exhibit 'inner city' problems.
The City has been pursuing policies to tackle these problems and

the rejuvenation of the City Centre and environmental improvement will, it is hoped, go hand in hand with the building of Metrolink.

The objectives of Metrolink may be summarised as to:

1. Improve accessibility to the City Centre.

2. Improve cross city links.

3. Complement other railway works eg Windsor Link and concentration of services on Piccadilly Station.

4. Complement City proposals for improving the environment, including increasing pedestrian dominated areas.

5. Help 'contain' car usage.

6. Act as a catalyst to new development in parts of the conurbation and redevelopment in the City.

7. Create more jobs.

Ultimately it is hoped that the Metrolink network will include some six or eight lines radiating from the City Centre. Most of these are existing suburban railway lines, but some will be new lines. The ultimate network may be around 100 route km in length. The first phase - to which this Paper refers - will incorporate two existing railway lines radiating from the North and South side of the City Centre respectively.

ROUTE

Phase I will incorporate the whole of 15.9 km Manchester Victoria to Bury line and 10.4 km of the line from Altrincham to Cornbrook Junction. These two existing lines will be connected by a new section 3.1 km long, together with a 0.7 km branch from Piccadilly Gardens to Piccadilly railway station. A new grade-separated junction will be built at Cornbrook to take Metrolink under the existing line from Manchester Oxford Road and Piccadilly to Warrington and Liverpool. The opportunity will also be taken to incorporate a 'flying junction' on Metrolink itself so that a possible future extension to Trafford Park and Salford Quays can take off from the Altrincham line. The section between Navigation Road and Deansgate Junction will consist of two parallel single lines: one Metrolink and one BR. This section together with the two level crossings will be under the control of BR with the Company having running rights including the use of the Bay platforms at Altrincham.

The first 1.73 km from Cornbrook Junction to the G-Mex Exhibition Centre (formerly Central Station) will use existing, but disused, bridges and viaducts. However extensive refurbishment works - and some complete renewals - will be necessary. A new work - the G-Mex Ramp - will then take Metrolink trains from the former rail level down to street level at the rear of the Holiday Inn/Midland Hotel. There will also be a new bowstring girder bridge over Great Bridgewater Street. Both this and the G-Mex Ramp itself are subject to consultation with the Royal Fine Arts Commission.

The remainder of the new route - 1.37 km - will be at ground level and will re-introduce street-operation into the UK. Part of it will be classified as LRT 1, i.e. street running with other traffic and part will be LRT 2, i.e. street running but segregated by kerbing from other traffic. There will also be some short sections of LRT 3, i.e. completely segregated. LRVs will be driven 'on sight' in the City Centre obeying traffic lights in the normal way, although there will be some degree of priority built into the system. At Piccadilly Gardens there will be a triangular junction where the 'branch' to Piccadilly (BR) station will take off. In due course it is hoped to extend the line beyond Piccadilly to serve the East and South-East of the conurbation.

The central section will be common to the whole of the Metrolink Network. All elements are thus being designed and built for the ultimate system where up to 24 trains per hour in each direction may be operating, although half that number is expected at Phase I. The power supply and overhead will be designed for upgrading to take future enhanced service levels. Wherever possible span-wire construction will be adopted, thus obviating the need for poles. However where poles are necessary, they will be integrated with lighting columns and other traffic furniture wherever possible. The overhead line - carrying the 750v DC traction current - will be at a 5.5m (minimum) above the roadway and will comprise a single contact wire only.

Currently the Altrincham line is worked by 3-car EMUs (Types 303 and 304) operating at 25kv AC overhead. These units were built in 1959/60. The Bury line operates on a unique 1200 DC third-rail, side contact system, pioneered by the Lancashire and Yorkshire Railway in 1916. Both this and the 2-car EMUs (Type 504) built in 1959 are life-expired. Both lines will be converted to 750v DC overhead operation (the option of being converted to 1500v DC having been dropped). This will involve installation of an overhead catenary system on the Bury line and from G-Mex to the bridges and viaducts going towards Cornbrook Junction. The existing overhead system on the Altrincham line can be converted with minimal effort.

STATIONS

Currently there are 9 stations on the Altrincham line and 9 on the Bury line. One or two more stations may be built on each line. On new sections stations will be built at: G-Mex, St Peter's Square, Mosley Street, Market Street, High Street, Victoria, Piccadilly Gardens and Piccadilly (BR). The new city centre alignment permits the construction of a station at Shudehill should development in the area justify this. Thus at Phase I it is expected that there will be 25 stations in all. There is also provision for a new station at Cornbrook between G-Mex and Cornbrook Junction.

It is a requirement of the Passenger Transport Authority (PTA) that the whole Metrolink system must be accessible to all people, including those whose mobility is impaired. This requires suitably-graded access ramps or lifts to stations and level entry/exit from platform to LRV. Since the majority of stations are former BR ones with a high platform (approximately 915 mm above rail) a high platform, high floor car solution has been adopted. However at certain locations in the City Centre such a design is felt to be too intrusive by the City Planners and, consequently, a 'profiled - platform' has been developed specially by GMPTE and its architects.

All stations must be able to accommodate a train made up of two LRVs, a maximum overall length of 60m. For the profiled-platform in the City Centre the 'high-spot' 915mm above rail and giving level access/egress between platform and LRV - will be adjacent to the two central doors on the leading car. Ramps up and down to the 'high-spot' will not exceed 5%. The remainder of the platform will be at 400 mm above rail. The LRVs will have a sliding step at an intermediate level, thus the maximum step ambulant passengers will have to make is about 250 mm. The 'low' section of the platform will be carefully integrated into the surrounding levels. All stations will have two canopies, designed to blend in with the city-scape.

Detailed surveys were undertaken of all the existing railway stations both with regard to their structural condition but also relating to the need of making them accessible to all. Altrincham and Bury are both Interchanges developed earlier by the Passenger Transport Executive (PTE) and require little work. However the remaining stations all require some work doing on them. All are too long for Metrolink's requirements, although a platform length of 120m, sufficient for a train of 4 x LRVs (in case of emergency) will be retained. The remainder of the platform and redundant buildings will be demolished. At many stations it is possible to gain level access to existing platforms by making an opening in an existing wall, in other cases access ramps will have to be built. Gradients on these will not exceed 5% (DIPTAC minimum 8.33%) and there will be level 'resting places' every 10m. At some locations it is either impossible to provide ramps, or ramps would be of excessive length or they would be too intrusive. In these circumstances lifts will be built. These will incorporate security and anti-vandal measures. Where cost-effective existing station awnings will be refurbished. All stations will have the equivalent of two shelters/canopies.

SIGNALLING AND CONTROL

On the segregated, largely former railway sections Metrolink will be fully signalled by a two aspect automatic system incorporating trains tops. In the City Centre from G-Mex Station to both Victoria and Piccadilly, LRVs will be driven 'on-sight'. One train will be able to come right up to the rear of another if circumstances permit or require this. LRV drivers are in sole command, subject only to traffic lights and certain aspects of the Highway Code, GMPTE's own Powers (through its various Parliamentary Acts) and the Tramways Act 1870.

The whole of the Metrolink network will be monitored from an Operations Centre to be built adjoining the Depot at Queens Road, just North of the City Centre adjacent to the Bury line. Trains will automatically and continuously identify their position onto a diagram in the Operations Centre. Thus at a glance, the Controller, will be able to see the whole operation. Equipment in the system will be programmed to identify out-of-course running, be it late or early. The Controller will be required to take a positive decision as to what action to take. All movements and decisions will be recorded in hard copy for subsequent analysis.

Trains will route themselves at junctions and into platforms at turn-back points. The diagram and/or train number will be keyed into a computer in each car and passive equipment laying between the rails will interpret commands and activate the points. Similar equipment will detect the passage of trains in the street sections, this 'releasing' traffic lights after the passage of a train. Such equipment will be able to detect whether a train is made up of one or two LRVs.

All LRVs will be fitted with radio and thus drivers will be able to contact the Operations Centre or vice versa at any point on the system for whatever reason. Controllers will be able to get in touch with all LRVs or individual ones. Many staff will also have mobile radios. In addition to supervising the operation of Metrolink the Operations Centre will supervise staff rosters and changeovers, amending as necessary; power supply and distribution; station security through CCTV surveillance; operation of lifts, escalators etc; vehicle allocation and adjustments thereto and the general safety and security of the system, its users and the staff. It will also maintain, through 'Hot Lines', direct links with the Greater Manchester Police and Greater Manchester Fire Services Control Centres. There will also be direct links with the City Engineer's Urban Traffic Control Centre and BR's main signalling centre at Manchester and the new signal box at Deansgate Junction.

ROLLING STOCK

The Light Rail Vehicles (LRVs) will be 29m long and 2.57m wide. They will be of a new, unique design and built by the Firema Consortium in Italy. They will seat 86 passengers and have a standing capacity (@4/m) of 120 giving a Nominal Capacity of 206. There will be two wheelchair spaces per LRV, adjacent to the second door in the direction of travel. There will be a tip-up seat in each space for use when not occupied by a wheelchair. Seats will be arranged in a 2 + 2 format all facing frontwards in the leading section and rearwards in the trailing section. The cars will be articulated and carried on three bogies, the outer two being powered.

The LRVs will have a maximum speed of 80 kph and initial acceleration and braking rates of 1.3m/s/s. The LRVs will be fitted with automatic couplers enabling them to be coupled and uncoupled from the cab. There will be a driving cab at each end and they will be one-person operated. There will be four, externally-hung sliding doors. These will be 'released' by the driver but will only operate at the request of a passenger inside the car or on the platform. Beneath each door there is a sliding step for use at low platforms. Their operation will be synchronised with the operation of the door. The doors will be 'locked' before a train is able to move and will remain so until the driver releases them at a station. The doors will have a two-speed closing mechanism so as to ensure that people (however small) or things are not trapped in them.

FORECAST USAGE

The forecast usage figures were provided initially by the PTE. Within two years of opening Phase I of Metrolink is expected to be carrying about 12.5m passengers per year. Peak hour flows are expected to be around 2,500 passengers with peak quarter-hour flows of 800 passengers. However the GMA Group undertook their own forecasts at the second stage of the tendering.

COMFORT STANDARDS

The PTA/PTE have specified that no train should exceed its Nominal Capacity (206 passengers per LRV) in the peak hour. In the peak quarter-hour the Nominal capacity may be exceeded by 30%. At no time should have a passenger have to stand outside the central area, other than by choice, for more than 15 minutes. There will be no smoking on Metrolink. In addition to carrying wheelchairs, Metrolink will also carry prams, pushchairs and shopping 'buggies'.

PASSENGER INFORMATION

Each LRV will have front and rear destination equipment operated from the leading cab. The LRVs will be fitted with Public Address equipment enabling the driver to talk to the passengers. He will also announce each station. All stations will be equipped with Public Address which will be triggered by an approaching train. Selected stations will have passenger information displays giving details of the time to the next train and the details of the train approaching. These displays will also be able to show time and advertisements.

SERVICE PATTERN AND FREQUENCY

The PTA/PTE specified the minimum frequencies they required to be operated over Metrolink in Phase I. These were:

	Monday-Saturday Throughout Day 0600-2400	Monday-Friday Peak	Sundays/Holidays
Bury-Whitefield (exclusive) Altrincham-Timperley (exclusive)	10	10	15
Whitefield-Piccadilly Gardens Timperley-Piccadilly Gardens	5	5	15
Piccadilly Gardens-Piccadilly	5	5	7.5

Within these parameters GMM can operate whatever service it considers commercial. The Company proposes to operate a basic 10 minute interval service throughout the day from Bury to Altrincham via Piccadilly and vice versa. In the peak hour this will be overlaid by another 10 minute integrated to give a 5 minute interval service running direct between Bury and Altrincham i.e. avoiding Piccadilly (BR). This will provide a 5 minute frequency in the peak period. Initially all trains are likely to be made up of one LRV.

FARES AND TICKETING SYSTEM

As part of the arrangement required by the Department of Transport and agreed between GMPTA/GMPTE and GMM, the fares charged by the Company on Metrolink are entirely a matter for them, as is their marketing strategy. It will be for the Company to negotiate any through ticketing arrangements with BR or bus operators.

The only requirement of the PTA/PTE is that Concessionary Passengers must be carried at the concessionary fare currently applicable. The company will be reimbursed on the basis of being 'no better nor no worse off', as required by the Transport Act 1985.

Passengers will be encouraged to pre-purchase tickets, at a variety of discounts both from Company and PTE offices and, subject to negotiation, from other agents or operators. Passengers requiring to buy a ticket at time-of-travel will purchase one from an automatic ticket vending machine (TVM). A Zonal fare structure is likely to be adopted since this facilitates through booking. The TVMs to be built by Thorn-EMI, will be simple to operate, will accept a full range of existing and proposed coinage, will give change and be robust. Their status and condition will be individually monitored from the Operations Centre. They will incorporate a 'molest Alarm' and be scanned by CCTV.

The 'open station' system, high-level of pre-purchased tickets/passes and the use of TVMs requires there to be a high level of ticket checking at all times. In turn this requires backing up by a 'standard fare' (exceeding the maximum fare a bona fide traveller would normally pay). The target will be for Customer Service Inspectors to check between 10% and 15% of all passengers. This team of Inspectors will have other jobs to be related to passenger care and information. They will also be qualified to drive. It is also likely that some of them will be part of the same group as the Controllers in the Operations Centre thus increasing job satisfaction and enabling the Company to respond flexibly to operational requirements and market demands.

OPERATIONAL PROCEDURES

Operationally light rail combines features of rail and bus operation. On the segregated sections it is a more flexible form of traditional or 'heavy' rail operation and on the street-running sections it is a more disciplined form of bus operation. No system exists currently in the UK with these features and thus GMM will be developing these from scratch. This is novel, exciting and challenging. However we have and will continue to seek advice from our colleagues at Blackpool, in Tyne and Wear and in Docklands.

The development of operational procedures (Rule Book, Operators Handbook, Manuals for all the major technical elements, etc) must go hand in hand with the detailed design of the system and its building. Modifications in any of the systems may require adjustments to operational procedures; it will be an iterative process. The two year time scale also requires job specifications to be prepared, staff to be recruited, trained and, in many cases, examined. The company will require to satisfy the Railway Inspectorate as to the appropriateness of all these procedures and the management structure, monitoring arrangements and lines of reporting.

MAINTENANCE ARRANGEMENTS

The company will be responsible for the maintenance of all features of the Metrolink system for the whole of the concession period. As Operator it will be responsible for the safe operation of the system and for the safety of the passengers, staff and general public. All the assets must be maintained in 'as new order' allowing for "fair wear and tear". In all aspects of refurbishing existing structures and facilities and design and building new items care is being taken to minimise maintenance requirements, since capital works are publicly funded whereas revenue items affect the profitability of the operation.

A new depot, centrally located for Phase I and for the ultimate development of the system will be built at Queens Road. The initial fleet of 26 LRVs will be maintained here, and there will be storage sidings, although it is expected that some LRVs will over-night at Bury and Altrincham. All LRVs will return once a day to Queens Road for internal and external cleaning. The maintenance shed equipped with pits and lifts will also include a wheel turning lathe for in-situ turning of LRV wheels. Facilities will be laid out in such a manner as to permit easy expansion at subsequent stages.

The Operations Centre and Company offices will also be located at Queens Road adjoining the Depot. There will be classrooms, canteen, mess room and toilet facilities. There will also be the driver and staff signing on and off points.

The arrangements for track and overhead line maintenance together with maintenance, painting and cleaning of structures and stations as well as the 'gardening' aspects have yet to be determined.

STAFF RECRUITMENT

Phase I of Metrolink is likely to require about 160 staff in total. The object is to have a small, flexible and well-remunerated workforce. The precise number and type of jobs the flexibility between jobs, skills and disciplines together with job descriptions and person specifications are currently being developed. As with operational procedures this is, to some extent, an iterative process, going along hand in hand with the design and build side of the contract. It is expected that a high proportion of the workforce will be qualified to drive LRVs. The Company is very keen to develop a 'team approach' and a well-motivated, proud staff. Recruitment will be open to anybody who is suitable subject to health and acceptability. All other things being equal people working on existing public transport in the Bury and Altrincham corridors will be given special consideration. Since staff costs are a major element in Metrolink's budget, it is essential that the build-up of staff is closely coordinated with the planned commissioning and build up of commercial operations.

STAFF TRAINING

Irrespective of from where they come or their age and background all staff joining Metrolink will require training: their previous employment will to some extent, influence the training programmes. These training programmes will go along hand in hand with the development of operational procedures and staff recruitment. All staff will attend a short Induction Course so that all may be familiar with the DBOM approach to the commercial operations of Metrolink.

A crucial factor will be to inculcate the Company's ethics from the very start. Metrolink is not just a new mode of transport with new features and new equipment it is a new approach to the provision of mass transport. Indeed the work 'mass' transport will be used to get away from some of the rather tawdry reputations that affect so much of 'public service' in this country at the moment. This is not to belittle the efforts of many in public service, public transport in particular, but we must be aware of the 'Customer Care' approach adopted by British Airways and some of the progressive bus operators.

There will also be the need for specialist training particularly in the fields of maintaining the LRVs sophisticated traction equipment and Metrolink's state of the art signalling and control systems. The training of all staff who hope to qualify to drive LRVs will be particularly crucial. They will require to be fully conversant with all procedures on both the segregated and street running sections. Safety training and training to deal with all aspects of emergencies will also be vitally important. Once operational there will also be the need for refresher courses and re-examination from time to time.

ORGANISATIONAL STRUCTURE

The GMA Group has established a new Company - Greater Manchester Metro Ltd - to design, build, operate and maintain Metrolink. The Board consists of representatives of the four parent companies and a Chief Executive and two Directors. The Chief Executive is responsible for the DBOM contract, although the Design and Build part is undertaken by a 'Supply Group'.

The Operations Director is responsible for setting up the whole of the operation, ie planning, marketing, recruiting, training prior to the operation of the system. He is also responsible for all the paperwork, programmes and procedures that go with this.

The Commercial Director is responsible for budget, both capital and revenue, for all the Contracts and Agreements between the DBOM elements and the PTE, for the business development through the letting of concessions, development and other commercial opportunities. He was also responsible, with others, for establishing GMM and all the legal and financial arrangements that have to be made before a Company can trade, eg opening a bank account.

The establishment of the Project and Site offices at Queens Road, following planning approval, the connection of the utilities, etc was the responsibility of AMEC. These offices were available from 1 February 1990.

Because of the nature of the contract the make-up of the Company will change over in time. Initially emphasis will be on design and build and, consequently, upon a whole range of engineering skills. As the design element runs down and the building element progresses, the operational and commercial side will build up. The size of the staff will grow as people are recruited prior to training, commissioning and trial running. The design and build side is the responsibility of the Project Manager, a civil engineer. There is a Deputy Project Manager who will be responsible for electrical and mechanical works. The implementation of the Metrolink scheme will be monitored by the GMM board so as to ensure completion of the design and build phases on time and within budget. They also have the responsibility to ensure that there is a suitable trained and qualified workforce to commence operations on the planned date – September 1991 for the first section.

WORKS TO BE CARRIED OUT

Two years is not a long time in which to carry out the detailed design and to build and equip the first phase of Metrolink. The major works that have to be undertaken are:-

- Conversion of the Bury-Victoria line to LRT including the replacement of the existing 1200 volt DC third rail side contact system with 750 volt DC overhead equipment.

- New operations and maintenance depot at Queens Road with facilities capable of being expanded to undertake all potential LRT lines.

- Reinstatement of the former Central Station (now G-Mex) approach viaduct and re-use of the former railway alignment to Cornbrook Junction. New track, signalling and OHLE being provided over this section together with a new station at G-Mex.

- Construction of the G-Mex Ramp and the bridge over Great Bridgewater Street.

- Conversion of the Altrincham line from Cornbrook Junction to Altrincham to LRT including the replacement of the existing 25 KV AC overhead with 750 volt DC equipment.

- Construction of the Metrolink dive-under at Cornbrook Junction.

- Refurbishment of all the stations on the Bury and Altrincham lines.

- Provision of new rolling stock to serve the Phase I network.

- Associated works including improvements or modifications to existing stations, minor highway schemes etc.

- Installation of a new signalling system on the former BR lines and a Control system for the Phase I network.

TRANSITION AND COMMISSIONING

The above works have to be accomplished either in a busy, congested city centre or on an operational railway. Substantial parts of the work are either in residential areas or adjacent to

275

shops and offices. There are thus numerous restrictions with regard to operational periods, noise, dust, etc. There are also limits with regard to road closures and the consequential diversion of bus services.

The nature of the construction problem differs between the works to be carried out on the existing Bury and Altrincham lines and those to be undertaken in the City Centre. In the former case it is planned to operate BR's services for as long as possible and to have the minimum changeover period. However much has to be done during the changeover. For example final platform and OHLE works that cannot be done whilst BR loading gauge stock is operating. Once construction is complete the various elements must be commissioned individually and collectively prior to formal approval by the Railway Inspectorate. Qualified operational staff are required for the commissioning. Once commissioned further training and line familiarisation must be undertaken prior to carrying the first fare paying passengers.

In the City Centre the works have got to be designed so that they can be implemented through a rolling programme of construction. However the commercial life of the city also has to continue and regard has to be paid to bus services. The detailed design of the alignment, the track, its construction, the interface with traffic management measures, the location of platforms and pedestrian crossings all have to proceed at the same time. Careful reference has also to be maintained on the vehicle itself, particularly end and centre-throw.

The preliminary analysis proposes the commissioning of the Bury line first, followed by the City Centre section and finally bringing in the Altrincham line. Train services on both the Bury and Altrincham lines will have to be curtailed so as to give longer periods for work at weekends and overnight. Sections of single line working may be adopted during the day. However it is inevitable that both lines will have to be closed for a few weeks. It is hoped to reduce such a period to a minimum. One of the early jobs of the company is the determination of the final work programme for the project.

In parallel with the works referred to above and the construction of the rolling stock, it will be necessary to recruit and train staff. Thus actual training will not be able to start until the relevant work or piece of equipment has been completed/delivered, tested and accepted. It will be necessary to ensure that all staff have operated the system without any passengers on it so that any 'debugging' can take place. At every stage the Company has to satisfy the Railway Inspectorate that it is safe and competent before he can approve each section of the works.

MARKETING

Metrolink will be competing in the market place with private cars, taxis and deregulated buses for passengers. GMM is a 'one-product' company competing in numerous different market segments each with its own characteristics. Each part of the market must feel that "Metrolink is for them". Metrolink has to be personalised, tailor-made to suit the different markets. The main segments may be defined as:

Passenger types: Male/female; age; disposable income; car availability

Reason for travel: essential/non-essential; work; shopping; social; etc

Time of travel: early or late; peak; off-peak; interpeak; regular/casual

Since the PTA/PTE has specified the periods of operation and the basic frequencies, the Company must adopt fares and marketing strategies that will fill the trains profitably. If it does not, it will not achieve the profits that it estimated at the time of bidding for the concession.

The Company also has to address the question of Metrolink's position in the market place. Whilst ultimately there may be a 100 km network, initially there will be a two line system of 31 km with 25 stations. The commercial arrangements entered into with BR and the bus companies will be important to the role of Metrolink. Unfortunately through-ticketing and pricing for market segments make for a complicated system - particularly for cash transactions at time of travel - whereas, ideally, the simplest possible system is desirable. The marketing strategy and ticketing equipment will have to progress together.

PUBLIC AWARENESS

From its conception in 1984 the public have been kept informed as to the progress of the light rail proposals at each stage of their development. Firstly, of course, each stage has been approved by the elected Members of the PTA who, in turn, have kept informed the City Council and the various Metropolitan Borough Councils. Members have been involved in numerous public meetings. The PTE - and now the Company - have attended many meetings, both public and private, formal or informal, explaining LRT in general and Metrolink in particular. Press, radio and TV coverage has been substantial.

Although we think that the public are aware of Metrolink's coming there is nothing like a bit of 'action' to concentrate the mind. In the late summer/early autumn of 1988 a programme of trial trenches were undertaken in the City Centre. At the end of February 1989 a major programme of service diversions was begun. Dotted white lines began to appear along the alignment of Metrolink showing the swept-path of the vehicles. People then really began to think that it was 'for real'.

With construction works now underway the public cannot fail to be aware of the approach of Metrolink, but this is a difficult time with things tending 'to get worse before they get better'. The Company, together with the client GMPTA/GMPTE, are working hard to stress the benefits Metrolink will bring and to tackle the inevitable complaints about disruption during the construction phase.

Through a policy of 'open-ness' which has been the hallmark of the awareness campaign, it is hoped to keep the public fully-informed and therefore sympathetic to Metrolink prior to its launch and formal opening.

SAFETY AND SECURITY

Safety and security have always been important in public transport. However recent events have elevated safety to an even higher plane whilst ever-increasing reports of assaults are raising people's awareness of the importance of security. Even without this scenario it has always been clear to the PTE and, since the award of the contract, the Company, that re-introducing street-running into the UK would require the utmost care and attention to detail.

Safety

The Metrolink system must be safe to its own staff, to the passengers using it and to the public at large. Safety has to be built into the system, accordingly all aspects of the works, be they rebuilding and refurbishing existing facilities or building new ones, are being designed and built to make them safe from all points of view.

If the system has been built with safety in mind then it must be operated safely. Thus the recruitment, selection, training and examining of staff and the managing of the system must ensure that all staff are aware of the importance of safety. In addition to discussions with the Railway Inspectorate meetings have been held with both the Greater Manchester Police and Greater Manchester Fire Service. Their advice has been sought and, where appropriate, approval of both the physical works and operational arrangements. The safety features stemming from the foregoing largely cover the safety of the staff and passengers.

The safety of the general public, particularly in the City Centre is of crucial importance, if the public (and their elected representatives) are to be satisfied. In the detailed design of the Metrolink alignment through the City Centre great care has been taken to protect the non-users, ie pedestrians, cyclists and motorists. The siting of stations, the arrangements at junctions, the positioning of kerbs and 'refuges', the traffic signalling arrangements and the paved areas all have been developed with the safe operation of the system in mind. Special care and thought has been given to those members of the public whose mobility is impaired in any way. Continental experiences show that light rail and others using the City Centre can co-exist safely and happily to their mutual advantage.

Security

To be cost effective it is essential that the numbers of staff on any public transport system are minimised. With LRT this means un-manned stations and LRVs operated by one person. This is normal LRT practice worldwide. However it is essential that passengers using the system feel safe and know that they are safe.

This is crucially important if the system is to carry the forecast number of passengers (particularly females, the young and the old) at off-peak times, especially after 1800 hours (1600 hours in the winter). That this comment is a sad reflection of society today is, regrettably, of no consequence.

All stations-entrances, platforms and, where they cannot be avoided, subways or 'dark corners' - are under continuous CCTV surveillance. The display screens are in the Operations Centre and all cameras are 'polled' on a frequent basis. The Controller can select any particular station and see what is happening. All stations have public address. From a security angle a controller can speak to the intending culprit before the assault or damage takes place. On each platform there will be an emergency call point linked directly to the Operations Centre as well as a staff telephone.

In the LRVs the drivers will be able to speak to the passengers and are in radio contact with the Operations Centre. The Emergency Alarm in the cars will automatically activate a voice channel so that the passengers concerned can talk to the driver who can decide immediately on the action to be taken.

As has already been indicated there will be a high degree of ticket checking, thus Metrolink staff will be on and around the system continuously. Add to this the presence of cleaning gangs, roving inspectors and suchlike and you will see that there is quite a high presence of Metrolink staff.

As part of the operational planning, emergency procedures will be developed for detraining passengers from all major locations and particularly those that have difficult access. These procedures will be developed in conjunction with the emergency services. All staff will have training in these matters, including fire drill, and will also have periodic refresher courses.

CONCLUSIONS

This Paper has attempted to show what has been involved in setting up the Metrolink organisation in Manchester. The DBOM approach is new to all parties. It provides opportunities and challenges. When this is taken in the context of 'light rail', a mode with which people are unfamiliar in the UK, some of the problems can be anticipated. It is too early to comment upon the benefits of this approach. However the GMA Group and GMM have got off to a fast start and expect to open for commercial operation in the Autumn of 1991.

(**Disclaimer**: The views expressed in this Paper are entirely those of the Author and do not necessarily reflect the view of GMPTE, GMM or the GMA Group.)

Discussion on papers 16–18

DR L. LESLEY, Liverpool Polytechnic
The integration of bus and rail services in the UK is presently politically unacceptable. However, the new Metrolink Co., GMM, is part owned by GM Buses Ltd the largest bus company outside London. Would it make commercial sense for GM Buses to redeploy buses away from routes parallel to Metrolink lines, to feed and distribute passengers from Metrolink in the suburbs? This would reduce GM Buses' unit costs (by operating in free flowing suburban traffic) and increase patronage (and profits) on Metrolink. But in 15 years time when Metrolink is handed back to GM PTE, then GM Buses and GM PTE will be competitors!

D. S. HELLEWELL, Paper 18
Decisions by GM Buses Ltd as to whether or not they revise their route pattern to feed/distribute to and from Metrolink stations is entirely a matter for their commercial judgement, both as a company in their own right and as one of the shareholders in Metrolink. However, in coming to their decision they will also have to have regard to the fact that they are themselves competing in the market place. If they withdraw a through service to feed Metrolink then another operator may well replace that service. Under a deregulated regime of bus operation one always has to have regard to what one's competitors might do and to try to minimize their commercial opportunities. The problem in 15 years time will no doubt be addressed then. Who knows; by then the legislative framework may be different.

J. Glover, Colin Buchanan & Partners
Mr Dixon told us that the public do not know what light rail is. Mr Taplin told us that 48 towns and cities want it. The conference has shown the difficulties that lie in the way.

DISCUSSION

The crux of the matter seems to be: does what the cities think they want match with what can realistically be provided? The challenge for us collectively as professionals is to marry up expectations with results, and to do so in a way which is profitable, safe, economical, reliable, legal and above all beneficial to the community.

D. S. HELLEWELL, Paper 18

I would put Mr Glover's question the other way round. Each city, town, conurbation has got its own unique transportation problems and priorities for their solution. The problems are multi-faceted, i.e. do not just relate to one issue, such as congestion. It is essential therefore that the authorities concerned identify clearly the problems to be solved. They then need to address the possible solutions. Whilst LRT will frequently offer a solution, it will not always be the most cost-effective answer. At the present time there is a grave risk that LRT, being the 'in-mode', is expected to provide solutions to all problems. Whilst LRT is very flexible and can solve many problems cost-effectively, it is not realistic to think that it can solve them all.